# THINK WELL, FEEL GREAT

# THINK WELL, FEEL GREAT

## 7 b-Attitudes That Can Change Your Life

Donald Norfolk

MICHAEL JOSEPH
London

MICHAEL JOSEPH LTD
Published by the Penguin Group
27 Wrights Lane, London W8 5TZ, England
Viking Penguin Inc., 40 West 23rd Street, New York, New York 10010, USA
Penguin Books Australia Ltd, Ringwood, Victoria, Australia
Penguin Books Canada Ltd, 2801 John Street, Markham, Ontario, Canada L3R 1B4
Penguin Books (NZ) Ltd, 182–190 Wairau Road, Auckland 10, New Zealand

Penguin Books Ltd, Registered Offices: Harmondsworth, Middlesex, England

First published 1990

Copyright © United Health Promotion Ltd, 1990

Typeset in $10\frac{1}{2}$ on $12\frac{1}{2}$ Linotron Novarese by
Wilmaset, Birkenhead, Wirral
Made and printed in Great Britain by
Richard Clay Ltd, Bungay, Suffolk

A CIP catalogue record for this book is available
from the British Library

ISBN paperback 0 7181 3133 9

'To my grandchildren Charlotte, Lisa, Olivia and Timothy, for whom I can wish no more than that they might be blessed with the qualities highlighted in this book.'

The cure of the part should not be attempted without treatment of the whole. No attempt should be made to cure the body without the soul, and if the head and the body are to be healthy you must begin by curing the mind, for this is the greatest error of our day in the treatment of the human body that physicians first separate the soul from the body.

PLATO

# CONTENTS

# Part I

# Chapter One:

# THE PHILOSOPHY
# OF HEALTH

The quest for health and happiness is universal. We all long to suffer less illness, have more vitality, feel fewer aches and pains and enjoy greater contentment and peace of mind. To obtain these priceless gifts scores of health-seekers today are leading lives of desperate abstinence and self-denial. Many exist on starvation diets. Some make regular pilgrimages to health clubs where they 'pump iron' until their muscles burn. Others stand on their head, jog, eat ginseng, puncture their skin with needles, drink glasses of sea water, irrigate their colons, steam in sauna baths, roll in the snow, fast, lie on sun beds or sleep on pillows filled with herbs. Since we live in a materialistic age, we feel certain that our salvation lies in the discovery of more effective *physical* treatments and *physical* cures.

It is difficult for anyone born in the age of heart transplants and test-tube babies to recognise the limitations of modern scientific medicine. We are aware of the desperate frailty of our lives and have a deep need to believe that our survival can be entrusted to a powerful force outside ourselves. Our forebears put their trust in God. We place our confidence in science. With touching faith we credit today's physicians with the power to control the forces of life and death. In times of adversity we look to them, rather than to priests, for healing and support. We expect GPs to find potions to cure our ills, soothe our pains, allay our anxieties and raise our moods of deep despair.

Yet the truth, which we stubbornly refuse to recognise, is that modern, technological medicine can do little to prevent chronic disease; less still to prolong life, and nothing at all to promote fitness, happiness and health.

The early physicians looked at man as a whole, an inseparable amalgam of body, mind and spirit. The modern scientist is trained to view him as a mechanical assembly of systems and organs. In hospital he becomes a prostatic carcinoma or coronary infarct, a process of reductionist thinking which makes it easy to lose sight of the humanity and unique psycho-social background of each individual patient.

Many doctors are aware of the dangers inherent in this dehumanising process and are once again espousing the principles of holistic health care. 'It is much more important to know what sort of patient has the disease, than what sort of disease the patient has,' said Sir William Osler, the famous nineteenth-century Canadian physician. But this change in outlook is not easily achieved, for the view of medical scientists is conditioned by the instruments through which they look. A gastroscope is an excellent tool for detecting stomach ulcers, but a useless instrument for revealing the causes of the gastric ulceration. It cannot detect that *this* person with a gastric erosion is eaten up with anger over the unjust treatment they have received in their parent's will, while the next cannot stomach their failure at work, or has lived through so many years of domestic disharmony that they are literally 'stewing in their own juice'. In the same way the microscope used in a pathologist's laboratory can expose malignant cells but is powerless to reveal malignant emotions – unfulfilled dreams, hidden fears, pent-up anger, unresolved conflicts, frustrations, bereavements, disappointments and harboured resentments. Yet these hidden psycho-social factors are a major cause of disease today.

As a result of adopting a mechanistic approach to health care we have become obsessionally conscious of the *physical* causes of sickness – lack of exercise, smoking, obesity, poor nutrition and excessive alcohol consumption – but generally unmindful of the *mental* factors which now play a predominant role in disease production. 'We have forgotten that man's spirit is the fundamental ingredient in his well-being,' says Dr Patrick Pietroni, Senior Lecturer in General Practice at St Mary's Hospital Medical School, London.

Our ancestors were plagued with epidemics which were normally spread by physical means – dirt, disease-carrying vermin, infected foodstuffs and impure water supplies. Improved standards of hygiene have largely eradicated these ancient plagues. In their place we have been overtaken by an epidemic of psychosomatic and stress-related disease which cannot be cured by removing the handle from the pump of an infected well or by the wholesale slaughter of colonies of black rats.

We still live in a polluted environment, but the pathogens which infect our contemporary world are not the *Pasteurella pestis* and *trypanosomes* but anger, fear, greed, bitterness and anxiety. These destructive mental attitudes – spread by television, radio and the daily press rather than by malaria-bearing mosquitos and plague-carrying rats – are the disease harbingers we have to fear today.

Most doctors and health educators have been slow to appreciate this growing threat to our well-being and equanimity, largely because their scientific training has conditioned them to believe that disease can be conquered by physical means. As a youngster I was a keen athlete and sportsman and grew up with the confidence that human beings could be kept in the peak of condition by a regime of regular physical training and sensible eating. When I became an osteopath I cared for my patients' bodies with the assiduousness and pride of a racing car mechanic, confident that they would function impeccably providing I kept their engines tuned and their bodywork in good repair. So certain was I of the value of this approach that I embarked on a second career, working as a writer, lecturer, and broadcaster in order to preach the gospel of physical fitness to the widest possible audience.

But gradually disillusionment set in. Contrary to my expectations there were people who remained unwell despite faithfully following my instructions. They ate the right foods and yet continued to be chronically tired. They carried out their aerobic exercises three times a week but still they could not shake off their chronic bouts of depression or anxiety. They complained of indigestion, insomnia and recurrent tension headaches despite their strict observance of the laws of physical fitness. What was going wrong?

To find an answer to this conundrum I decided to study not the sick but the people whom I considered were conspicuously well. I turned initially to my elderly patients, some of whom were enjoying a level of health and happiness in their nineties which was a source of envy to people many years their junior. What was the secret of their success? None I discovered were health fanatics or fitness freaks. Few had followed strict diets or strenuous exercise routines. But all maintained a cheerful disposition, a positive outlook and an exuberant zest for life. Was this cluster of mental traits responsible for their remarkable vitality?

To evaluate this possibility I re-examined the reports of gerontologists who have analysed the habits and life-styles of those remarkably lively centenarians living in the mountain villages of Ecuador and Caucasia. This confirmed my earlier suspicion, that a healthy attitude of mind is a far more important determinant of health than a healthy pattern of physical behaviour. When Dr David Davies, of London University's Unit of Gerontology, visited the vigorous old stagers living in the Vilcabamba district of Ecuador he found that they were not particularly abstemious and were breaking several of our cherished health laws. Many smoked cigarettes made from tobacco grown in their own gardens and drank anything from two to four cups of unrefined rum a day. Yet these vigorous oldsters were still fit to work well after their hundredth birthday. They knew nothing about dietary science or human physiology and made no attempt to improve their health by following a macrobiotic diet or joining a yoga class. Yet they maintained a far higher level of fitness than the health gurus of the Western world. Their lives were long and rich, not because they smoked or drank or ate a largely vegetarian diet, but because they had a healthy mental attitude, which Dr Davies described as 'bright, alert and active'.

A similar discovery was made by American gerontologist Dr Alexander Leaf, when he studied the sprightly centenarians living in the Caucasian mountains. A typical representative of the group was Khfaf Lasuria, a remarkably youthful 130-year-old, who was tending her chickens and pigs when Dr Leaf called. She welcomed him with traditional Georgian warmth and invited him inside her house where they toasted each other's health first in vodka and then in wine. Aided by an excellent memory she talked with great good humour about her past and present life. She had retired from full-time work two years before, but continued to be active in her home and garden. When questioned she could offer no secret recipes to explain her remarkable fitness and longevity. She did not sleep with her body facing due north, nor did she take daily supplements of minerals and vitamins. But she did have a healthy mental outlook, which was characterised by her friendly manner, cheerful disposition, independent spirit and active life-style.

Similar qualities were discovered when two German psychologists set out to discover the secrets of healthy survival by following the lives and fortunes of 200 senior citizens aged between sixty and seventy-five. At the end of fourteen years' detailed observation, the researchers analysed their results and found that the main characteristic of the survivors was that they had a more positive, active approach to life. They were also more adaptable and had a strong feeling of being needed by others and of use to society.

The message seems clear: that a healthy attitude of mind is a more important determinant of health than slavish devotion to dieting and physical fitness routines. This is the inference of numerous medical research programmes, analysed in subsequent chapters of this book, which suggest that the regular exercise of a sense of humour can do more to improve well-being than the repeated and monotonous flexing of muscles in a gym. In the same way it seems apparent that we are more likely to enhance our health by stripping our lives of needless feelings of anxiety and inadequacy than by ridding our diets of sugar, salt and animal fats. This too is the inference of numerous medical research programmes, analysed in subsequent chapters of this book.

Unfortunately no financial gains are made by proclaiming this fundamental truth. Espousing the cause of mental well-being promotes the health of the individual, but it doesn't sell running shoes, exercise equipment or calorie-reduced foods. It also undermines the standing of the health professions and pharmaceutical industry, for once it is realised that we can influence our health by modifying our mental attitudes we will have less call for drugs, surgery and the whole expensive panoply of contemporary medical care.

In recent years we have made false gods of physical fitness cults. The Nautilus machine has become our altar, the gymnasium our temple. To propitiate the goddess Hygiea we have performed daily callisthenic rituals. We have mortified the flesh with aerobic exercise, 'feeling the burn' that earlier zealots experienced from self-flagellation. We have risen at dawn, and with thousands of other devotees we have donned the holy regalia of sweat-band, tracksuit and pumps to make withershins pilgrimages around athletic tracks and city parks from Boston to Bolton. (Joggers in the Northern hemisphere invariably choose to run in an anti-clockwise direction, a course which has always been favoured by celebrants of witchcraft rites.) Our baptism has been in sweat rather than in holy water.

This obsessive concern for physical fitness has produced its own crop of sickness, as ergonomist Dr Tom Reilly of Liverpool Polytechnic found when he studied the health records of a group of nearly a hundred women athletes ranging in expertise from recreational runners to international sportswomen. These women were running to keep fit, and to achieve high standards of physical performance, and yet in the previous year four out of five had suffered minor injuries which had prevented them training for an average of twenty-eight days. They had struggled to achieve superlative health and had ended up spending a month of the year hobbling about on limbs crippled with stress fractures, shin splints and Achilles tendon strains. If their sole goal was to break an international sporting record, it is possible to tolerate this suffering, just as one accepts frost-bite as an occupational hazard for Arctic explorers; but if their intention was simply to get fit it is impossible to find medical grounds to justify this high toll of self-inflicted suffering. The time has come for doctors to give a clear warning of the dangers of excessive exercise. It is not necessary to jog, lift weights or go to aerobic exercise classes to keep fit. In fact these activities – if carried to extreme – can present a genuine health hazard.

Over-exercise will make you tired, irritable and prone to infection. For women it can also have an adverse effect on hormonal balance, producing menstrual irregularity, infertility and retarded breast growth. Chronic tiredness is the price that many athletes pay for success in the highly competitive world of international sport. At the height of his career, long-distance runner Brendan Foster admitted: 'The trouble with distance running is that you're always tired, and the higher you aim the more tired you are.' This persistent exhaustion may be a sign of athletic commitment, but it is certainly not a symptom of health. Tests show that sedentary individuals can destroy 10 to 30 per cent of their red blood cells by indulging in bursts of unaccustomed strenuous exercise. No wonder they feel shattered after their first aerobic class, and take some days to recover from the damage caused to their oxygen-carrying cells. Why doesn't someone tell them that they can get all the exercise they need by going for a brisk walk round the park?

Why punish your body with physical exercise when it can do you more harm than good? Dancing a foxtrot with someone you love in your arms is heavenly; enduring the pangs and punishment of an hour-long aerobic exercise routine can be hell. Chasing after a dog is fun; plodding round a marathon course is generally little more than blatant self-abuse. Even the early gurus of aerobic exercise, like cardiologist Dr George Sheehan, author of *Running and Being*, admit that the physical benefits of running have been grossly exaggerated. 'I think that jogging is completely unnecessary', is Sheehan's view today. 'A good brisk walk is equivalent to a jog any time.'

The gladiators of the athletic stadiums are prone to sporting injuries, and also appear to be unusually liable to coughs and colds. Like thoroughbred racehorses and pedigree dogs, they seem to be bred for display in the show ring rather than for everyday performance. Dr Reilly found that 80 per cent of his group of women athletes had suffered illnesses during the previous year – chiefly colds and flu – which put them out of action for an average of eleven days. 'Illnesses were more pronounced in those doing the hardest training,' he reported. 'The suggestion is that strenuous activity does suppress the activity of the immune system.'

An equally disturbing by-product of the physical fitness movement is that it is creating a battalion of anxious hypochondriacs. Health is expressed through the free and joyous use of the total personality, not through a neurotic concern for the functions of the body. Life is for living, not for keeping a daily tally of calorie intake, pulse rate, bowel movements and blood cholesterol levels. We are well when we are happily unaware of the working of our body, not when we have to give conscious thought to the operation of our muscles, heart, lungs or spine.

According to health expert Dr Charles Sterling, Chief Executive Officer of the Institute of Aerobic Research in Texas, about 50 to 75 per cent of women who exercise seriously are liable to develop an 'unhealthy attitude' to fitness. The same degree of neurotic introspection can be found in devoted followers of other health cults, such as nature cure, nudism, postural re-education and vegetarianism.

Even medically controlled programmes of health education can be more liable to provoke anxiety than to promote health. In one campaign a group of over 1,000 adult Americans was subjected to a programme of instruction designed to make them more aware of the dangers of uncontrolled high blood pressure. After a year's course of instruction – mediated through lectures, discussions and informative leaflets – it was found that the campaign had misfired. Instead of being healthier the indoctrinated group had developed *higher* blood pressure than a control group which had received no specific education about the hazards of hypertension. Inadvertently the researchers had received an insight into the working of the human mind. From the well-informed subjects they learned that people given an excess of health information can worry themselves sick. From the uninstructed controls they received the timely reminder that there are times when ignorance can be both bliss and beneficial therapy.

Here is one field in which a little knowledge can indeed be a dangerous thing. This even applies to habits as detrimental as cigarette smoking, where it appears to be better to be a carefree smoker than an obsessive non-smoker, constantly worried about the insidious hazard of passive smoking and aggressively antagonistic towards any nicotine addict who has the temerity to pollute the air they breathe and think they own. This was shown by a ten-year research project at Heidelberg University, under the direction of Professor Hans Eysenck. It revealed that age for age the death rate of prejudiced non-smokers was almost three times higher than that of smokers who adopted a relaxed policy of live-and-let-live. This provides further evidence that unwholesome habits of thought are more damaging than unhealthy habits of physical behaviour.

We seek for physical fitness and run the risk of becoming neurotically preoccupied with the working of our bodies. In our search for health we embark on crash slimming diets, and become depressed. Three months later, when we give up the struggle for beanpole slimness, we find that we are heavier than before. We shun dairy foods to reduce our risk of coronary disease and find that we are becoming deficient in calcium. We seek health with the fanaticism of pilgrims seeking the Holy Grail. As the quest becomes increasingly obsessive we develop into fitness fanatics and food freaks. If one diet fails, we quickly try another. If an exercise regime proves unsuccessful, we waste no time switching to an alternative system, exchanging dumb-bells for rowing machine, or running shoes for static bicycle. Never for a moment do we question the path we are taking. We have been so conditioned to accept the promises of the physical fitness movement that we remain convinced that health and happiness will be ours if only we stop smoking, breathe more deeply, shun polluted air, exercise a little harder, shed a few more pounds, sit in ergonomically designed chairs, consume more vitamins, avoid foods which contain artificial additives, drink water fresh from mineral springs, sleep on orthopaedic beds, flood our offices and homes with negative ions and cover our bodies with clothes woven from natural fibres.

While most of the sanitary practices undertaken are beneficial, they are of trivial significance compared with the etiological factor which forms the subject-matter of this book. In the pages which follow evidence will be amassed which proves that the powerful antidote to sickness is not exercise, dieting or abstinence from smoking but a healthy mental attitude.

The Greeks and Romans took a more truly holistic approach to health. They stressed the importance of *mens sana in copore sano*: a healthy mind in a healthy body. We, perhaps because we are living in a grossly materialistic age where drugs and medical science reign supreme, have endeavoured to achieve health of body without first establishing health of mind. This is where our health crusades have failed. This is why millions of people in the Western world are existing in a state of sub-health despite the vast sums of money that are spent each year on health care.

In frustration and bewilderment we turn to politicians and scientists to provide a remedy for this great morass of sickness. We petition the state to provide better hospitals. We urge the pharmaceutical industry to develop more effective drugs. We lobby industry to create a healthier working environment. We pressurise doctors to provide more effective medical care. But the solution lies not with 'them' but with 'us'.

**A healthy attitude of mind is the single most important factor in the promotion of health and the prevention of disease.** This is not something which can be bought in a chemist's shop or health food store. This is something we must create for ourselves.

We realise that faulty patterns of thinking can provoke a wide range of psychosomatic *disease*. Why are we *so* slow to accept the potency of the *mens sana* concept as a source of psychosomatic *health*? We know that *negative* thoughts can produce hex deaths. Why are we not equally aware of the life-giving power of *positive* thoughts?

I firmly believe that the harnessing of this inner force will be the major medical development of the twenty-first century; an advance which will be more beneficial to man's well-being than the discovery of antibiotics. This will be the penicillin of the Aquarian age.

Chapter Two:

# THE MIND
# THAT HEALS

Scientific medicine is a powerful tool, but its powers are puny compared with the healing power of the human mind, which has been protecting man for millions of years. Long before we learnt to put our trust in surgery and drugs, man had faith in the therapeutic potency of the human psyche.

The early Jews believed that sickness was the punishment for sin. Physical ailments arose, not because individuals were eaten up with disease but because they were consumed with greed, lust, envy and anger. These were dubbed the mortal sins because their long-term effects were recognised as deadly. As the Rabbis warned: 'There is no death without guilt, and no suffering without sin.' None of the twelve tribes sought to overcome their ailments by eating starch-reduced matzos, or jogging daily around the perimeter of the temple. Healing was obtained by freeing the spirit, not by disciplining the body.

Jesus Christ observed this ancient Judaic tradition throughout the course of his healing ministry. When a youngster suffering from muscular paralysis was brought to him on a stretcher, he could have asked him to carry out a set of muscular strengthening exercises, or advised his helpers to stimulate his withered limbs by applying electric eels, a primitive form of faradism favoured by the Roman physicians of the day. Instead he chose to attack the root cause of the disorder by saying: 'My son, your sins are forgiven.'

Most primitive tribes recognise the ease with which the body can fall prey to the effects of mental sickness. Some cultures ascribe their debility, depression and pain to devil possession; others to the workings of the evil eye. The Cakchiquel Maya Indians of Guatemala ascribe many of their ailments to *susto*, which means fright sickness. This disease appears in as many physical guises, all of which stem from psychological states of anxiety and fear. Other sickness arises when the Cakchiquels fall under the spell of a *brujo* or witch. In these instances the Mayas know that relief cannot be found from Western-style drugs, but from a visit to a native healer or *curandero*, who knows how to deal with the evil eye and alleviate pathologies of the soul.

Freud was equally aware of the protean expressions of psychic distress, which could produce symptoms ranging from insomnia and impotence to headaches and hysteria. As a scientist he could not bring himself to believe in *susto* and *brujos*. Instead he postulated that disease arose when the subconscious mind was enthralled by neurotic longings, hidden fears, unresolved conflicts and long-repressed guilt – a theory which the Cakchiquel Indians might be forgiven for considering little better than their own!

Others have accepted the psychogenic origin of disease, but have placed the blame on demon possession rather than neurosis or fear sickness. One of the most powerful evil spirits to terrorise the lives of the ancient Babylonians was Lilith, the demon of wind. Mothers were fearful that Lilith would enter their babies during the night and cause them pain and colic. So the women of Babylonia adopted the precaution of singing chants as they rocked their infants to sleep to keep the demon Lili-at-bay, a term which gradually became corrupted to 'lullaby'. In other cultures devil possession was overcome by exorcism rites, the efficacy of which were closely related to their charismatic qualities and their ability to stimulate the healing powers of expectation, faith and hope. Excavations of ancient burial grounds reveal that in the pre-Freudian era, when there were no psychiatrists to exorcise the hobgoblins of the mind, people had their skulls trepanned to allow the escape of evil spirits. In one graveyard 120 skulls were unearthed, six of which had been trepanned. Given the primitive medical instruments of the day, the lack of anaesthetics and the complete absence of aseptic precautions, it is incredible that anyone should have been willing to have a hole bored in their skull, and even more amazing that so many should have survived the ordeal, a fact which can be deduced from the frequent evidence of post-operative bone growth. Such was the popularity of the procedure that one can only assume that it was a highly effective form of health promotion, a deduction which in itself is a remarkable testimony to the curative power of faith and psychogenic healing.

These views on the aetiology of disease held sway for centuries. They lost their popularity, and gave way to the belief that sickness was chiefly the product of physical agencies, only in the wake of the epochal discoveries of the last century. The process was hastened by the contributions of men like Edward Jenner, the vicar's son, who discovered that the injection of pus drawn from the hand of a milkmaid suffering from cowpox could give protection against smallpox. This introduced the concept of prophylactic immunisation, a technique which has been responsible for saving millions of lives throughout the world. Some years later Louis Pasteur, the son of a French tanner, showed that the bite of a rabid dog could provoke hydrophobia. This demonstrated that diseases could be spread by germ transmission and so laid the foundation of the science of bacteriology. Madame Curie's discovery of radium produced a powerful tool for the treatment of cancer. Penicillin, isolated by Fleming and Florey, led to the development of a wide range of antibiotics. The discovery of vitamins underlined the importance of malnutrition as a cause of sickness. This was followed by the production of insulin by Banting and Best, which offered a cure for diabetes and also showed that diseases could be caused by hormonal imbalance or deficiency. Anyone living through this exciting period could be forgiven for investing the medical scientist with an aura of omnipotence, and for believing that the remedy to the age-old problems of unhappiness and sickness could be found by providing a better diet, a cleaner water supply, a more sterile environment or a higher standard of personal hygiene. But physical utopias do not produce health, nor do they provide a panacea for disease.

We have made large strides towards conquering the world's major infectious diseases – smallpox, dysentery, tuberculosis, malaria and typhoid. Better nutrition throughout the affluent world has made relative rarities of diseases such as scurvy, rickets and pernicious anaemia. Hormone supplements have provided a means of controlling maladies like diabetes, myxoedema (a degenerative condition due to a defect in the thyroid gland) and Addison's disease (disease of the adrenal glands). Yet, despite these brilliant achievements, our health remains poor. We still die prematurely – often before our biblically allotted three score and ten – from heart disease, infection and cancer. To find an answer to these killer diseases we delve more and more deeply into the pathology of the *body*, when it now seems certain that we would be more profitably employed making a closer study of the effect of morbid states of the *mind*. To emphasise this point, let us consider the aetiology of these three causes of premature death – coronary disease, systemic infections and malignant growths.

The Western world is plagued by an epidemic of heart disease. One fashionable explanation for this outbreak is our increased consumption of animal fats. In response to the urgings of dieticians we have stopped eating eggs, given up butter and hard cheese, exchanged white meat for red and switched to drinking skimmed milk and spreading our bread with margarines made from polyunsaturated vegetable fats. In the process we have run the risk of becoming deficient in calcium, since 60 per cent of our traditional intake of this bone-strengthening mineral comes from dairy foods. This may help to explain the increased incidence of osteoporosis, the bone disease associated with lack of calcium which is responsible for nine-tenths of the fractures occurring in British women over the age of forty-five.

In answering the health educators' pleas we have given up much and achieved little. People have gone on stringent diets to reduce their intake of saturated fats and found that this has made no significant difference to their blood cholesterol levels. Others, for test purposes, have gone on high-fat diets with no disastrous consequences. In one trial a group of volunteers was asked to eat a daily ration of three eggs, which provide the richest dietary source of cholesterol. This produced no significant increase in their blood cholesterol levels. Why then do we continue to emphasise the role of the diet in the prevention of heart disease, while ignoring the importance of such factors as stress, emotional excitement, frustration and pent-up anger?

We are encouraged to treat cholesterol as a rogue chemical. Yet this substance is vital for the formation of the bile salts, the steroidal sex and stress hormones and the fatty sheaths which provide a protective covering for the nerve fibres. To maintain supplies of this essential raw material the body has the ability to manufacture cholesterol within the liver. In practice most people today create far more cholesterol in their livers than they ever obtain from their diet. This is especially true when they are under stress, for blood cholesterol levels are far more sensitive to emotional upheaval than they are to dietary change.

If a sample is taken of a racing driver's blood before the start of a Grand Prix race it will often appear milky white because of its high fat content. This is an automatic response to the pre-race excitement and an integral part of the 'fight or flight' response, which floods the bloodstream with calorie-rich fats which provide excellent fuels for strenuous muscular exercise. The same thing happens to accountants when they are working under pressure towards the end of the fiscal year, when they may show a doubling of their blood cholesterol levels.

During periods of mental strain our bloodstreams become loaded with animal fats of our own creation. Fat levels rise at these times, not because we are indulging in a surfeit of buttered buns and cream cakes, but because our bodies wrongly assume that we need a sudden output of energy-rich fuels to help us cope with the crisis they are under. This atavistic response had a protective value when our forebears roamed the primeval forest and came face to face with a sabre-toothed tiger, but it has little point today when we suffer stress which can rarely be relieved by violent physical action.

A number of reputable scientists, noting the association between heart disease and high blood cholesterol levels, have jumped to the conclusion that the one must be a direct outcome of the other, rather than an accompanying side-effect. This is a totally fallacious – *post hoc, propter hoc* – argument, which is no more valid than suggesting that caffeine is a major cause of aircraft accidents, since most pilots have drunk one or more cups of coffee in the twenty-four hours preceding the crash of their planes.

Health educators have become so firmly convinced of the causative link between fatty diets and heart disease, that they have unwittingly doctored the evidence to support their case. Men in the industrial north of England have an above-average risk of heart disease and high blood pressure. This, according to government health officials, is because they have a liking for fatty food. In recent years, the media in Britain gave great publicity to the 'bangers, butties and chips' theory, but chose to ignore a subsequent dietary study which showed that the consumption of fat was actually *lower* in the north of England than elsewhere in the country. They also failed to make allowance for the high level of unemployment in the industrial north, which was subjecting men to the constant mental strain of boredom, job uncertainty, financial insecurity and loss of self-esteem. These factors were overlooked by the visiting health workers, but not by the northerners themselves. 'I suppose if you have a lot of men worried about whether they are going to keep their jobs, then that leads to stress', was the verdict of the mayor of the industrial town with the highest rate of hypertension. A similar explanation was given by the mayor of the rural town with the lowest level of hypertension. He was equally convinced that high blood pressure is more closely related to what goes on in the mind than to what goes into the stomach. 'We have won the distinction for our flowers and how polite we are,' he told reporters. 'These things are vital to the quality of life and probably help our health.'

And what of the mass of epidemiological evidence? The Swiss live in a stable, peaceful and prosperous society which has witnessed a 22 per cent decline in male deaths from heart attacks, during a period when the consumption of fats actually *rose* by 20 per cent. Irish workers who emigrate to America, and have to adapt to a new and faster way of life, have a greater risk of coronary disease and high blood pressure than their brothers who remain behind, even though their stay-at-home siblings consume more milk, butter, fat and calories. The Amish farmers of Pennsylvania live in a close community which is largely untouched by the pressures of modern society. They own no cars, possess no radios or television sets, have no regard for clocks and watches and feel no compulsion to compete with their neighbours. But they do eat a very rich diet, full of dairy foods and animal fats. According to contemporary dietetic theories they should be prime candidates for coronary disease; whereas in fact their bucolic life-style is rarely troubled by cardiovascular disease.

Despite this wealth of circumstantial evidence, we are still asking people to make major modifications in their physical life-style to protect themselves from coronary disease. But the results do not justify the upheaval and expense. In 1972 the US National Heart, Lung and Blood Institute undertook a massive study of the effectiveness of health care programmes aimed at eliminating coronary risk factors. Starting with a group of nearly 13,000 middle-aged men who were judged to be high-risk candidates for heart disease, they assigned half to a special intervention programme. These targeted men received counselling to encourage them to reduce their use of cigarettes and to lower their intake of cholesterol. In addition they were given drug treatment to reduce their blood pressure when this was found to be raised. The other group was given no special treatment or advice. Ten years later, when the fate of the two groups was compared, it was found that the intervention programme had made no significant difference to the coronary death rates, except in one alarming respect. When the researchers analysed the results they discovered that the men in the first group who had received drug treatment for hypertension or ECG abnormalities had a death rate which was 57 per cent higher than the untreated group. This raises the alarming possibility that these were cases of iatrogenic death, produced as a side-effect of the medication they had received. For these unfortunate men the medicine had almost certainly proved more lethal than the disease.

The theory that fat consumption is a major cause of heart disease would have sunk into obscurity long ago, had it not been for the blind enthusiasm of health educators, aided by the marketing zeal of firms who have a vested interest in promoting the sale of low cholesterol foods and the drug companies which stand to make a fortune out of selling drugs which lower blood cholesterol levels. Even physicians find it difficult to accept 'that what a man feels, perceives and believes may be as important as what he eats or inhales in the causes of clinical coronary disease'. That is the opinion of Dr Meyer Friedman, the Californian cardiologist who, together with his colleague Dr Ray Rosenman, has played a major role in drawing the world's attention to the importance of mental factors in the aetiology of coronary disease. These two pioneers have found that people of a certain emotional disposition are particularly prone to heart troubles. The dangerous qualities they have identified are a combination of aggression, ambition and excessive concern with the passage of time, an obsession which they call 'worry sickness'. To this cluster of traits they gave the now well-established term 'Type A behaviour'. Experience taught them that this mental set was the major determinant of heart disease, a cause more important than all the commonly advanced physical factors, such as obesity, lack of exercise, smoking and an excessively fatty diet. This assertion was so contrary to recognised medical teaching that it was difficult for other doctors to accept.

So, to establish the validity of their claim and to counter the doubts of their colleagues, Friedman and Rosenman, embarked on a ten-year study of 3,500 men. At the outset they divided the men into two personality groups: the assertive, hard-driving Type As, and the more relaxed, easy-going Type Bs. Once this preliminary classification had been made, they then investigated the men's physical health and established whether or not they smoked, how much exercise they took, their blood cholesterol levels and the nature of their diet. They then sat back to await the course of events. In the decade which followed, over 250 of the previously healthy men suffered a heart attack. The vital question was: could these calamities have been foreseen from the original screening tests? A detailed review of the data provided over-whelming support for the researcher's hypothesis, as Dr Fried-man reported: 'Did the dietary data we obtained at the beginning help us to predict who was most apt to succumb later to heart disease? Not at all! Did the amount of exercise they took help us to discern those who later fell prey to heart disease? Not at all! In fact the only sign of undisputed prognostic value was the men's mental make-up. When the final analysis was made it was discovered that the men in the initial Type A group were *three* times more likely to suffer heart disease than those who had originally been classified as Type B personalities – irrespective of whether or not they smoked, were overweight, inactive or overfond of fatty food.

The layman will not be too surprised by these findings, for folklore has always recognised a close link between the emotions and the function of the heart. When we fall in love our 'heart skips a beat'. When we are afraid our 'heart stops still'. When we are bereaved we become 'heartbroken'. When we are disappointed our 'heart aches'.

What may be more difficult for the average person to accept is the link which exists between the mind and the onset of infectious disease. We have been brought up to accept without question the germ theory of disease. Infectious diseases, we know, are caused by bacteria and viruses, not by states of mind. They may be related to the dirt and squalor of the external physical environ-ment, but not to loneliness and fear or any other disorder of the internal, mental environment. Yet, the rapidly developing science of psychobiology is proving that the mind plays a major role in determining whether or not we succumb to infectious disease. The outcome of this perennial battle between microbe and man is determined not only by the virulence of the bug but also by the resistance of the host.

People who are depressed may fall prey to infections which they could successfully combat if they were in rude health and cheerful frame of mind. The Bavarian scientist Max von Petten-kofer demonstrated this with great panache when he challenged the theories of Robert Koch. Koch was anxious to prove that cholera was not caused by inhaling impure air, but by infection with a water-borne micro-organism. Pettenkofer ridiculed this suggestion. Tiny creatures might be found in dirty water, he conceded, but these were not the cause of cholera. To prove his point he invited Koch to provide him with a concentrated sample of the bug, cultured from a cholera victim. This he mixed in a glass of water and swallowed with a dramatic flourish. Apart from a bout of mild diarrhoea, Pettenkofer suffered no ill effects. Nor did several others who repeated his bold experiment. They survived simply because the cholera germ was powerless to flourish in resistant bodies.

Laboratory experiments confirm that mental stress impairs resistance to disease. If monkeys are injected with a foreign protein they protect themselves by producing appropriate anti-bodies. But this natural defensive response is impaired if their mental equilibrium is disturbed by exposure to batteries of noise and bright, flashing lights – the sort of stress that city dwellers experience every day of their lives! Further research on the same lines was carried out at West Point military academy, when scientists from Yale University investigated 1,400 cadets to see whether stress affected their predisposition to glandular fever. Immunological tests carried out at the start of the trial revealed that roughly a third of the group had so far escaped contact with the virus. As the study progressed a number of these disease-free subjects developed glandular fever antibodies, showing that they had come into contact with the Epstein-Barr virus. But only a quarter of these newly infected cadets developed clinical signs of glandular fever. Why had some been smitten, while others had survived? The researchers scrutinised their findings and discov-ered that the disease did not strike at random. The cadets who lost their battle against the virus were the ones who claimed to be under the greatest pressure with their academic work. In many cases they suffered because there was a discrepancy between their aims and their abilities. They were highly motivated to perform well, and had often inherited the high standards of over-zealous parents, but they lacked the talent to achieve their goals. This combination of lofty aspirations and modest ability set them an unrealistic task and placed them under continual pressure which people of lesser ambition or greater talent did not experience.

Surveys reveal that mental attitudes, as well as stress, can depress the effectiveness of the immune system. Sometimes a cheerful disposition can prove a better antidote to sickness than antibiotic drugs. Volunteers attending the Common Cold Research Unit, Salisbury, have been infected with rhinoviruses and then subjected to a number of provocative treatments. They have been made to wear damp socks, sit in sodden clothes or take a bath and then linger for thirty minutes in a chilly corridor clad only in a wet, skimpy costume. Following these ordeals about a quarter have developed the classical symptoms of a head cold, described so vividly by Charles Dickens as 'deaf in the ears, hoarse in the throat, red in the nose, green in the gills, twitchy in the joints and fractious in temper'. Others have escaped unscathed. What gave them their superior immunity? Dr David Tyrell, the Unit's Director, says: 'If you are an introvert, you get worse colds than if you are an extrovert.' If you are the victim of depression and social isolation your chances of contracting a cold are increased. If you have a cheerful, optimistic, friendly disposition you are less likely to develop a running nose and streaming eyes.

Happiness also seems to be a defence against cold sores, caused by the *herpes simplex* virus, according to a survey carried out among a group of student nurses. This showed that irritating cold sores broke out more frequently on the mouths of nurses who described themselves as 'typically unhappy' than they did on those who claimed to be blessed with a more cheerful disposition.

Since stress and mental attitudes impair the efficiency of the body's immune system, it is not surprising that they can also precipitate the onset of cancer. Diets low in fibre and rich in meat, nitrates and alcohol are believed to predispose to cancer. But in the eternal fight against the Big C we must never forget that *what* we eat is almost certainly less important that what is eating us. Alcohol may erode the oesophagus and stomach, but unhappiness, bitterness and fear eat into the soul and disturb the balance of the body's neurohormonal system. This was shown many years ago when doctors in New York studied the life histories of cancer patients, and found that their tumours were frequently preceded by 'loss of the central relationship and a sense of utter despair, and a conviction that life held nothing more for them'. The association between malignant growths and long-standing feelings of helplessness and hopelessness is a theme which recurs in many cancer studies. The link is so pronounced that it can even be used as a guide to determine whether suspect growths are malignant or benign. This was shown when two New York doctors investigated a number of women with suspicious growths on the neck of their wombs. They showed that the outcome of their tests, and the identification of cancerous growths, could be predicted with reasonable success using the sole criterion that malignancies are more likely to develop in women who have recently experienced feelings of hopelessness.

Other doctors have discovered that cervical cancer is three times more likely to occur in women who have been separated or divorced than in those who have maintained a stable marital relationship. Closer investigation has revealed that the link between cancer and unhealthy attitudes of mind is partly hormonally based. For some while it has been recognised that women who have high levels of corticosteroids (hormones with a cortizone-like action) and low levels of circulating androgens (hormones governing the development of the sexual organs) have an above-average risk of succumbing to breast cancer. An American study, published in the Annals of the New York Academy of Sciences, reveals that this unhealthy hormonal balance is commonly found in women who are worried, apprehensive, despairing and afraid. The prognosis is far better when a lower level of corticosteroids occurs in conjunction with a higher titre of androgens. This balance is found in women who are hopeful, self-assured and who possess a strong faith either in God or in the fates.

Given the right mental attitude, we can escape heart attacks, conquer cancer and survive plagues. Healthy-mindedness is the most powerful medicine we have, and the most neglected of all twentieth-century therapies.

# Chapter Three:

# THE HEALTHY PERSONALITY

The Greeks knew nothing about viruses and bacteria, but they did recognise that personality plays an important part in the origins of sickness. Hippocrates believed that a person's predisposition to disease was determined by his/her underlying character, which he divided into four basic emotional types – the choleric, the sanguine, the phlegmatic and the melancholic. Galen, another giant of the ancient medical world, noted that a close link exists between cancer and melancholia. These early physicians had a truly holistic approach to health care, and sought to achieve a wholeness of body, mind and spirit.

The drive to achieve this state of balanced excellence had the support of both the Greek educational system and the prevailing Greek culture. Greek youngsters of both sexes were encouraged to take part in gymnastics, dancing, archery, wrestling and athletics, activities which formed an integral part of their training programme. The aim was clear. 'Good education,' wrote Plato, 'is that which tends most to the improvement of the mind and body.' They recognised that bodily health is conducive to mental hygiene, but were equally aware that fitness of mind predisposes to the well-being of the body. Plato sought to emphasise the importance of this psychosomatic mechanism, which remains a major cause of human misery and sickness. 'My belief,' he wrote, 'is not that the good body by any bodily excellence improves the soul, but, on the contrary, that the good soul, by her own excellence, improves the body as far as this may be possible.'

Unfortunately our modern approach to health education is so heavily biased towards the physical causes of disease that we often fail to recognise the damage caused by pathological attitudes of mind. The school curriculum today provides for the development of the body as well as the culture of the mind, but the two subjects are kept entirely separate. Games periods and physical training sessions are separate entities, rather than integrated parts of an holistic development programme. And where nowadays is the training in the life skills – ethics, philosophy, logic, music, poetry and rhetorical debate – which played so large a part in the development of the cultured Greek?

Historical records enable us to trace the education of a typical well-born Greek. The young man, named Theodore, was born on the shores of the Black Sea. Until the age of fourteen he enjoyed the normal primary education of the day. Then his father died and his widowed mother decided to send her young son to Neocaesarea to study rhetoric. Once he had mastered this subject he travelled to Beirut to carry out an eight-year study of Roman law. This was followed by a period of personal tutoring under Origen, the great Christian philosopher. Here he studied astronomy and geometry to deepen his appreciation of the wonders of God's creation. Further study of ethics, philosophy and the scriptures developed his moral character and enabled him to achieve 'a godlike mastery of body and soul'. Our modern schooling is largely devoid of this broad training in the humanities and life skills. We are channelled into being mathematicians, engineers, computer programmers or doctors. And so we are sent out into the world, well prepared to make a good living, but ill prepared to make a good life.

The citizens of ancient Greece and Rome emphasised the culture of the body, but they did not do so out of context. By the third century BC there were nearly 800 *thermae*, or public baths, within the confines of the city of Rome alone. These 'palaces of the people' were infinitely more popular than our modern health clubs and aerobic exercise studios. They also provided a far wider range of facilities, which were designed to culture the body and also to foster the healthy growth of the spirit and mind. The Roman bath at Caracalla, for example, had an excellently equipped gymnasium, numerous rooms for massage and a complicated series of hot and cold baths, but it also had a well-stocked library where visitors could improve their minds by studying the precious *volumina*. In addition it possessed gardens, works of art and promenades where people could listen to recitations of poetry and the discourses of the great philosophers. These were centres of holistic development and cultural excellence. As a result the Graeco-Roman world developed well-rounded individuals who placed as much emphasis on ethical standards and moral principles as they did on hygiene and physical fitness. Plato was a perfect example, a man who was not only one of the world's greatest philosophers but also a skilled athlete and a one-time winner of the wrestling competition in the prestigious Corinthian games.

Today we are beginning to acknowledge the need for a more truly holistic approach to medicine and cultural education, but we have much to learn and still more to un-learn. Medicine in particular has to overcome its preoccupation with the anatomical nuts and bolts of life, a blinkered outlook which it has cherished for over 300 years. This materialistic obsession can be traced back to Thomas Sydenham, an Oxford graduate who fought with Cromwell during the Civil War and who went on to achieve well-deserved fame as a physician in the city of Westminster during the middle of the seventeenth century. Prior to Sydenham, doctors had appreciated the existence of diseased individuals, but had done nothing to recognise the existence of individual diseases. This outlook changed when Sydenham kept a careful record of his patients' symptoms and noted that they occurred in regularly repeated clusters. These pathognomonic signs recurred whatever the person's status, age, sex, occupation or prevailing mental attitude. As a result doctors came to focus their attention on the *disease* rather than on the *patient*. Sydenham took his theory of disease specificity a stage further when he suggested that some diseases represented the triumph of hostile outside agencies.

Subsequent medical research has supported Sydenham's theories. Experiments have shown that specific illnesses can be caused by germs, allergies, chemical poisoning, vitamin deficiencies and glandular imbalance. These discoveries have made a major contribution to the combat of diseases such as cholera, painter's colic (lead colic), scurvy and diabetes, but have done little to combat the contemporary plagues of peptic ulcers, cancer, heart disease, depression and anxiety neurosis. Moreover, these mechanistic theories do little to explain why some people succumb to sickness while others survive, despite being subjected to the same bombardment of germs or the same level of nutritional impoverishment or environmental pollution.

Throughout our lives we are forced to face the malevolent influences within our environment. However hard we try we must come into daily contact with armies of potentially harmful bacteria, viruses, poisons, carcinogens, allergens and chemical irritants. Whether these chance encounters produce symptoms of disease depends not only on the virulence of the pathogenic agents themselves, but also on our inherent powers of resistance. When our health is threatened do we survive or succumb? It is becoming increasingly apparent that the answer to this vital question often depends on our state of mind. This is the crucial Factor X which so often determines whether we remain well or fall sick.

Doctors schooled in conventional methods of diagnosis are trained to discover fractured femurs but not to detect shattered dreams and broken hearts. A study of the attitudes of British doctors, carried out by the Department of Health and Social Security, revealed that medical practitioners 'display a remarkable inability to cope with anything but the most mechanical relationship with the patient'. Many have too little time to discuss their patients' social, emotional and spiritual problems. Others are too embarrassed, or consider themselves too inexperienced, to take on the role of father confessor, marriage guidance counsellor or sex therapist. When faced with psycho-social problems the average doctor finds it easier to treat the symptoms of the malaise rather than attempt to deal with its underlying cause. Hence the widespread abuse of psychotropic drugs, which are often dispensed as a face-saving convenience for the doctor rather than as a cure for his emotionally disturbed patient. This process was aptly described by one unhappy patient who said: 'I feel that when my doctor writes me a prescription for Valium, it is to put *him* out of *my* misery.'

This widespread neglect of the psycho-social parameters of disease has distorted, and sometimes even falsified, the medical profession's approach to health promotion. This is clearly demonstrated in its current attitude towards the prevention of heart disease, where it persistently underplays the damaging effects of chronic stress, and wildly exaggerates the risk of eating an excess of saturated animal fats. When Dr Meyer Friedman and Dr Ray Rosenman, the two Californian cardiologists mentioned in the last chapter, began their study into the origins of coronary disease they were not expecting to find that hearts could be damaged by adverse mental attitudes. 'Like all our peers,' they later confessed, 'we were not intellectually prepared thirty years ago to accept emotional stress as a relevant component of coronary heart disease.' Nevertheless they undertook their investigation with an open mind and discovered that people who exhibit Type A behaviour – who are ambitious, highly competitive, easily angered and time obsessed – have raised levels of blood cholesterol and a *seven-fold* increased risk of showing clinical signs of heart disease.

But the doubting Thomases within the medical profession refused to be convinced by this disturbing evidence. They did not want to acknowledge that mental attitudes played a major part in the causation of disease. So they clung to their cherished belief that a diet loaded with cholesterol was a prime cause of heart disease, a thesis which Friedman and Rosenman described, and still describe, as 'ridiculous'. To support this shaky theory they even resurrected an unfounded notion propounded by vegetarians during the Victorian era, that eating meat and other animal fats made men bloodthirsty and aggressive. Using this argument, and flying in the face of reason and common sense, they suggested that it was not the Type A behaviour which caused an

31

elevation of cholesterol levels, but the cholesterol-saturated diet which provoked the aggressive, Type A behaviour.

Even now the emphasis of coronary care programmes is still focused on making changes in *physical* life-style rather than on making modifications in *mental* attitudes. Why? Is it because doctors find it quicker and easier to advise people to lose weight, reduce their cholesterol intake and take up jogging, and time-consuming and embarrassing to counsel them to modify their unhealthy patterns of behaviour? Or is it because the vested interests of industry benefit vastly from the physical fitness movement, but stand to gain nothing from campaigns which seek to promote the concept of healthy-mindedness? Moreover, if the emphasis of health education switches to culture of the mind, what place will there be for the gurus of the physical fitness movement – the aerobic dance teachers, dieticians, specialists in sports medicine and the teachers of hatha yoga? Their essential message was that we are what we do and eat. The lesson we have to learn today is that we are primarily and essentially what we *think*.

The difference between these two outlooks is not a mere philosophical quibble; it is an issue which is fundamental to the development of medicine and to the allocation of scarce human and material resources. If we accept the new philosophy, then individuals rather than specialists will become responsible for their own lives, happiness, achievements, health status and their freedom from disease. This is a shift of responsibility which some will welcome and others fear. Surveys show that the average person suffers a recognisable medical symptom every third day of their lives. This may be a trivial complaint – a cough, a muscular twinge or a temporary skin rash. Nevertheless, if we are of an anxious or dependent nature, we could find justification for consulting a doctor 120 times a year. But if we adopt the principles of holism we will be forced to rely far more on our own resources. In future when we suffer disturbances – whether of body, mind or spirit – we will be asked to look within ourselves for both the cause and cure. This will involve a sometimes painful process of self-appraisal and emotional readjustment. Even our props will be stripped away. Our ancestors wore talismans to ward off sickness and the evil eye. We have adopted charms more appropriate to a scientific age, believing that we will be happy and free of illness providing we take our vitamin pills, go for a daily jog, do our Jane Fonda exercises, avoid eating chemically adulterated foodstuffs and clean our teeth with dental floss. This touching faith in material aids and external rituals will need to be replaced by a more far-reaching trust in the inherent powers of the body to heal itself – a force which the Greeks identified as the *vis medicatrix naturae*: the healing power of nature. The introduction of this new philosophy will have repercussions which are ethical and social as well as purely medical. It will emphasise the pre-eminence of the individual and the need to return to codes of behaviour which will benefit both the well-being of the individual and the health of the communities in which they live. Since the new philosophy is non-materialistic it will have an egalitarian effect, making the wise pauper as privileged as the multi-millionaire who can afford to visit expensive health farms and pay the fees of the world's leading medical consultants.

At present the medical world is showing an increasing interest in environmental medicine, and is attempting to determine the extent to which our health is affected by radiation, pesticides, atmospheric pollution, lead poisoning and the diminution of the earth's protective ozone belt. When the new philosophy is adopted, equal attention will have to be paid to the ecology of the mind. Already there is a profusion of evidence which demonstrates that our well-being is directly and profoundly effected by the psycho-social environment in which we live. In previous ages man succumbed to bacterial plagues – malaria, typhus and bubonic fever. Today he suffers primarily from mental plagues, caused by unhealthy attitudes of mind which are just as deadly as the germs of yesteryear, as the chapter which follows describes.

Chapter Four:

# THE DOMINANT MIND

No computer exists which can duplicate the myriad functions of the brain of *homo sapiens*: the wise animal. With the aid of our three-pound mass of neurons and supporting glial cells we see, hear, smell, taste, feel, move, think, remember, evaluate, create and plan.

Normally when we consider the powers of the human brain we think primarily of the functions of the cerebral cortex, the area responsible for the higher faculties of sensation, movement, speech, sight, memory and thought. This is the heavily convoluted region, shaped like two halves of a walnut, which writes poetry, solves mathematical problems, invents complicated electronic machinery, composes symphonies and remembers pages of Shakespearean prose. But there is a far more vital area of the brain – sometimes called the 'old' brain – which is often overlooked because it goes about its work quietly and unobtrusively. This is the subterranean control room of life rather than the showy hall of genius and learning, the region responsible for maintaining the life-preserving functions of the body – heartbeat, respiration, growth, control of blood pressure and blood sugar levels, hormonal output, immune response, temperature regulation, emotional expression and adaptation to stress. But the two regions are not disassociated. Our higher, cerebral centres have extensive connections with the 'old' brain. As a result, our thoughts, imaginings and fears have a profound influence on our biological functions. We may experience indigestion when we get annoyed at the thoughtlessness of our neighbours. We cannot 'stomach' their behaviour we say. Or perhaps we develop patches of eczema when we are irritated by parents whom we allow to 'get under our skin'.

Thoughts can make us ill, and thoughts can make us well. A healthy state of mind can preserve our lives, a sick mental attitude can hasten our demise. Eng and Chang Bunker were the original Siamese twins. Joined together at their midriffs they had no choice but to share their lives, work, play and even marital intimacies. When Chang died at the age of sixty-three, his brother was in excellent health – yet Eng died three hours later. His doctor could find nothing whatsoever to explain his abrupt collapse and advanced the opinion that he had been literally scared to death.

Sudden deaths like this can also be caused by witchcraft. The Arunta tribe of central Australia have developed a bone-pointing ritual which is capable of causing sudden death. Observers note that the Aruntas heighten susceptibility by uttering spells which threaten to split the victim's throat or tear his heart asunder. Once a state of acute fear has been induced, the *coup de grace* is administered by pointing the instrument of doom, which is generally a small bone bearing a few strands of human hair. This simple act is sufficient to cause the sickness and death of those conditioned to believe in the power of the evil eye.

Even sophisticated people, who have no truck with witchcraft or demonology, can be destroyed by fear. Several medical textbooks recount the tale of the student prank which went tragically awry. The youngsters held a mock trial which ended with one of their members being found guilty of a capital offence. The death sentence was passed with great solemnity and the doomed man was led to his place of execution where he was blindfolded and then suddenly and unexpectedly hit on the back of the neck with a towel. The shock blow, instead of bringing the jape to an amusing climax as was intended, brought about his instantaneous death.

These spectacular deaths are presumed to be due to functional changes, for no pathology or specific disease processes have been observed on post-mortem examination. Some doctors think the deaths are caused by 'vagal inhibition', others as a result of a disturbance of heart rhythm. Whatever the actual cause, there seems no doubt that we can indeed be scared to death, or have our hearts broken by sudden tragedy or grief.

Dr George Engel, of the Department of Psychology and Medicine at Rochester University, New York, has made a special study of deaths related to incidents of sudden emotional stress. Searching through the records he has discovered 170 separate cases of stress-induced deaths. These include a golfer who died while he was being congratulated for achieving his first hole-in-one, and a seventy-year-old man who suffered a fatal collapse at the start of a memorial concert marking the fifth anniversary of his wife's death. Even more remarkable was the case of the octogenarian who was enjoying the excitement of a reunion with his fifty-five-year-old son after a twenty-year separation. Both died within minutes of each other. On the basis of this evidence Dr Engel has no doubt that stress can prove fatal.

If we accept that thoughts and emotions can kill, we must accept the even greater possibility that adverse mental states can make us sick. Equally well we must recognise that if perverse thoughts have the propensity to make us ill, salutary thoughts have the potential to make us well and prolong our lives. It is safe to predict that the coming decades will see a growing appreciation of the enormous healing potency of the human brain, a realisation which will have a far greater effect on human health and happiness than all the previous, and much heralded, breakthroughs of medical science.

Pain is one of man's major afflictions. This is eased today with powerful drugs – aspirin, codeine, paracetamol and morphine. But pain is also sensitive to thought processes. It can be allayed by distraction and faith and exacerbated by loneliness and fear. Indian fakirs have trained themselves to lie on beds of nails.

Members of the Pardhi tribe of India's Deccan plateau prove their innocence by walking a set number of paces while stoically carrying a rod of red-hot iron. Elsewhere in the same region an annual 'hook-hanging' ceremony is observed, in which religious celebrants have hooks driven through their backs by the village carpenter so they can be paraded around the village swinging from a pole. Such is the state of religious fervour induced by the initiation ceremony – designed to make them *devas* or temporary gods – that they appear impervious to the pain. 'During the ceremony that I observed,' confirms one eyewitness, 'the celebrant was in a state of exaltation and showed no trace of pain.'

On Good Friday in the Philippines a similar demonstration of psychoanalgesia takes place, when Christian penitents allow themselves to be crucified on wooden crosses, with three-and-a-half-inch nails driven through their hands and feet. These remarkable examples of the power of mind over matter might be thought to be the preserve of a trained élite of Eastern ascetics; but experience shows that we *all* have the ability to master pain to a remarkable degree. If we choose we can suffer agonies from a pinprick or show indifference to major trauma.

Lt-Col. Henry Beecher of the US Army Medical Corps made an on-the-spot study of soldiers seriously wounded in the beach-head assault on Anzio. Some of the casualties had compound fractures; others had lost whole limbs or suffered hideously gaping abdominal wounds. Yet a third claimed they felt no pain at all and a further quarter described their suffering as slight. Even in their shocked and weakened state the men felt they had the inner resources to bear their suffering without medical aid. (All but 27 per cent of those in pain refused the offer of pain-killing injections.)

Dr Beecher admitted that he was 'puzzled' by what he found, especially when he discovered that the majority of the men accepted their mutilating injuries without complaint but 'yelled like hell' when approached by a medical corpsman armed with a syringe. In his report, published in the Annals of Surgery, he concludes: 'Pain is an experience subject to modification by many factors: wounds received during strenuous physical exercise, during the excitement of games, often go unnoticed. The same is true of wounds received during fighting, during anger. Strong emotions can block pain.'

Pain can also be reduced by mental imagery. Peter Carey suffered horrendous injuries when the plane he was flying in crashed into the face of a quarry. He escaped miraculously with his life, but experienced burns which destroyed all but a small portion of his face. In the months of plastic surgery which followed he suffered constant pain, as doctors struggled to reconstruct his missing nose, eyebrows and ears. He controlled the agony by practising a simple piece of mental trickery. 'I made myself believe that the pain was only in half of my body,' he explained. 'Every morning I would wake up and mentally drive the pain into, say, my left half. I would then think only of my right side. Next day I would drive it across to the right, and think only of my left. I found that, that way, I could live with the pain – it only seemed half as bad.'

Psychologists have discovered that people employ a number of ingenious ruses for blocking the perception of pain, produced by experimental procedures such as immersing the hand in freezing water or applying a tourniquet around the arm. When subjected to these discomforts one woman imagined that she was the *Venus de Milo*. Since she had no arms she could not feel the pain! Another subject imagined that his body had been transported away from the laboratory, where it escaped the painful stimuli. Others succeeded in numbing their arms by imagining that they had been given a pain-killing injection.

Dr Elmer Green, founder of the Menninger Foundation, carried out numerous experiments on pain perception and came to the conclusion: 'Pain control is to a large extent attention control.' One of his series of well-documented experiments involved Jack Schwarz, a dedicated Sufi. He could push six-inch steel needles through his arms without pain, and without producing any of the physiological changes normally associated with pain perception, such as increased respiration or quickened pulse rate. Equally remarkably the puncture sites did not bleed when squeezed as might have been expected, nor did they become infected, even when Schwarz rolled the needles on the floor with his shoe, as a jocular dismissal of the doctor's suggestion that aseptic precautions should be taken! How did the Sufi exercise this remarkable control over the normal sequelae of non-sterile puncture wounds – pain, haemorrhage and infection? His answer was simple. At the time of the experiments he merely imagined that his arm was not connected to the rest of his torso. Instead, when he inserted the needle into his skin, he conjured up the mental image of pushing it into a well-upholstered chair. In this way the chair received the damage rather than his arm.

Nowadays we rely on analgesic drugs and anaesthetics to relieve the pain of surgical operations because of their reliability and ease of administration. But in the first half of the nineteenth century, when chemical anodynes (curative measures which soothe pain) were not available, doctors carried out major surgery under hypnosedation, which in many cases proved a highly effective technique of pain control. In exceptional circumstances this method is still employed today.

A short while ago a woman was due to have cosmetic surgery on her breast. Since she was fearful of anaesthetics, her consultant agreed to operate under hypnosis. She slipped easily into a state of deep relaxation and was given the suggestion that her breast and chest wall would become completely numb, as it was when tested with pinpricks. On receiving this confirmation the surgeon took his scalpel and made an inverted T-shaped incision under her breast and up to her nipple. Folding back the two triangular flaps of skin, he removed a wedge of breast tissue and a layer of surplus fat and then set about the task of remodelling her breast. Throughout the seventy-minute operation the patient chatted happily with the operating team and showed no sign of discomfort or distress. When the bandages were being applied she chose to sit up, and with a smile said she had not felt a thing. In fact, as the surgeon said later: 'If there was any fear or apprehension it was felt by the operators rather than the patient.'

Hypnosis is a powerful tool, which can also be used to lessen or eliminate the pain of childbirth and dentistry. Here it has the advantage that it produces none of the usual side-effects of anaesthetics and pain-killing drugs. Moreover, whereas analgesic drugs merely deaden pain, hypnotic suggestions can be used for a wide variety of therapeutic purposes. With hypnosis the dentist can enlist the power of the patient's mind to reduce pain and also to lessen bleeding and salivation. In midwifery its applications are wider still. According to Dr F. L. Marcuse, past-President of the Washington State Psychological Association and a world authority on the medical applications of hypnosis: 'Hypnosis may reduce apprehensiveness about the birth process, relieve morning sickness, eliminate backache, decrease constipation, reduce vomiting, secure a greater degree of co-operation from a patient than is possible with drugs, obtain a reduction of some two to four hours of labour time and consequently of maternal exhaustion, lessen the pain of childbirth or sometimes banish it completely.' All these benefits, and they are not the product of advanced medical technology or pharmaceutical research, but of controlled thinking. We can frequently will ourselves free of pain, just as we can frequently will ourselves to have easy labours, trouble-free surgery, unblemished skin, boundless energy or a happy disposition.

Long before the advent of modern analgesic drugs, man eased his pains with a variety of bizarre folk remedies. He allayed the discomfort of fibrositis by placing slices of potato in his pocket, believing that the gradual blackening of the potato was a sign that rheumatic impurities were being drawn from his body. When he had severe lumbago he would tie a band of coloured material around his waist, knowing that this would form a magic circle which would give protection against the evil spirits which had entered his body and wracked his loins with the acute pain which the Germans still call a *Hexenschuss* or 'witch's blow'.

At a later stage faith was placed, not in pagan charms, but in holy relics. There is a charming story of a young Tibetan monk who was given the task of carrying a particularly holy tooth to a far-away monastery. On the way the precious relic was lost and the terrified youngster decided to replace it with a dog's tooth he chanced to discover. This he presented with some trepidation at the monastery, where it was installed in a magnificent reliquary. Here it gave rise to countless miracles. Within a short while the venerated object began to glow with a supernatural light, thereby providing proof of the old saying that even a dog's tooth will shine brightly in the eye of faith.

Nowadays we may scorn this primitive approach to healing, which we contend has no scientific basis and works only by inspiring faith and encouraging hope. But then exactly the same could be said of many of the wonder drugs we take today. An inert tablet of powdered starch can perform therapeutic miracles if it gains our trust and mobilises our inherent curative resources.

A firm's doctor set out to test the value of a tablet, which was being promoted as an effective cure for the common cold. To examine its value he divided the firm's staff into three groups. The first group was given the new remedy and the second an identical-looking dummy pill. The remaining employees acted as controls and received no treatment whatsoever. When the results were analysed it was discovered that the workers taking tablets had suffered fewer colds than the controls – a protection which was provided just as effectively by the dummy pill as by the one containing the active, cold-prevention ingredient! Obviously the positive response represented a victory of mind over matter, rather than a triumph of pharmaceutical wizardry. Given the right mental attitude of hope and trust we can stimulate the body's immune system to shrug off coughs and colds, and probably also to check the development of malignant growths.

This has been suggested by animal experiments, in which mice and rats have been hoodwinked into strengthening or weakening their immune response. In one set of tests, carried out at the University of Rochester Medical Center, rats were given saccharine-sweetened water together with a drug designed to reduce their immune response. Once their brains had grown accustomed to this conditioned response, the animals were given the sweetened water without the accompanying drug. The results proved identical. Even without the immunosuppressant drug the brain produced a lowering of the animal's resistance to infection. Parallel experiments have been performed at the US National Institute of Health, although in this case a batch of mice were trained to *increase* their immune response when exposed to the smell of camphor.

There seems no doubt that the body's immunity against infections, foreign bodies and malignant cells is under the ultimate jurisdiction of the brain, even though the control may be exercised in an exceedingly complex fashion through the intermediary of changes in autonomic nerve balance, neurochemical secretion or hormonal output. The same can be said of every other system of the body, for the brain is also the final regulator of the function of the heart, lungs, circulation, digestive system and endocrine glands. This explains why every disease to which man is heir can be amenable to cure by the three mental graces – faith, hope and love. This revelation has far-reaching implications in the prevention of cancer. Most oncologists (tumour specialists) believe that we are constantly waging a battle against rogue malignant cells, just as we are continually waging a war against germs. What matters is not the arrival of malignant cells within our body, but our ability to destroy them before they take a hold and multiply. This view is supported by the discovery that people given immunosuppressant drugs, perhaps to enable them to accept organ transplants without rejection, are eight times as likely to develop cancer.

Medical research has shown that placebos can be successfully used to treat headaches, hay fever, insomnia, seasickness, angina, high blood pressure, asthma, epilepsy, acne, arthritis, urticaria, constipation, diabetes and intermittent claudication (arterial disease of the legs). To exert their full power the patient has to have faith in the dummy pills and ideally also in the therapist. Vast numbers of people are dependent now on tranquillisers and are convinced that they could not cope with the maelstrom of life without these chemical crutches. Yet sophisticated medical trials have shown that the anxiety-relieving potency of Valium, the most commonly prescribed tranquilliser, is almost entirely in the mind. Tests carried out by Arthur and Elaine Shapiro at the Mount Sinai School of Medicine, New York, reveal that Valium has a very slight pharmacological effect initially, but after its first week of use the benefits experienced are all due to the placebo response. The strength of this curative mental response was found to depend on two factors – the positive attitude of the patient to the drug and the degree of trust they placed in the prescribing doctor, which was related to his or her status, physical attractiveness, enthusiasm, warmth, empathy and general likeability. Of these two factors, the patient's trust in the doctor proved to be three times more important than the faith they had in the dummy pill.

At one time doctors were well aware that their physical presence and charisma were an important part of the treatment they prescribed. To heighten their patient's trust they dressed in impressive clothes, decorated their consulting rooms with academic certificates and testimonials from eminent patients and spoke in a scientific language calculated to impress the uninitiated layman. Dr Franz Mesmer used all the tricks at his command to heighten the suggestibility of the patients who flocked to his opulent home in eighteenth-century Vienna. Dressed in long silk robes trimmed with gold lace, he would wave an ebony wand like a stage magician, dangle lodestone bars to attract the flow of animal magnetism, fix his patients with a penetrating stare and make stroking passes over their bodies to conjure up the healing fluence. Some branded him a quack, but with his particular brand of suggestive healing – which soon came to be called mesmerism – he enabled hundreds of people to rid themselves of their disabilities and pains.

Cagliostro was another of the great faith healers of eighteenth-century Europe. He too went to extreme lengths to surround himself with an aura of mystic power. He wore flowing robes and a tall turban, worked in a dimly-lit room filled with soft music and incense and peered into a crystal ball to summon prophetic visions. These were the trappings of a mountebank, but the gimmicks served the invaluable purpose of giving patients the confidence and strength of mind to cure themselves. The modern doctor shuns these unscientific aids. His patient's duty is to be a passive and faithful recipient of the drugs or therapy he orders thereby dividing the affairs of the body from those of the mind. This totally artificial dichotomy started with the philosophical concepts of René Descartes, who said: 'I consider the body as a machine. My thought compares a sick man and an ill-made clock with the idea of a healthy man and a well-made clock.' This simplistic analogy has its appeal, but also its pitfalls. The layman welcomes mechanical diagnoses – like slipped discs and fallen arches – because they are easily understood. They also appear to point the way to logical methods of cure. According to the followers of Descartes, disease is when a pathological spanner is thrown into the works of human robots. A quick twist from an osteopath will replace a slipped disc. A pair of well-made arch supports will shore up flat feet. But patients are beginning to resent being treated like mindless machines, and are coming to realise that doctors who maintain this impersonal approach are failing to utilise the most potent of all healing instruments – the human brain.

Medicine has benefited enormously by adopting the Descartian approach, but if it is to make further progress it must now embrace the concepts of an earlier philosopher, Theophratus Bombastus von Hohenheim, better known as Paracelsus. As a questing twenty three year old, Paracelsus set out on a grand tour of Europe and Asia in search of new ideas. 'The doctor must be a traveller,' he explained, 'because he must enquire of the world.' Twelve years later he settled down in Basle where he quickly gained a reputation as a gifted medical lecturer and prolific writer. On the basis of his revolutionary teaching he has been described as 'the Luther of Medicine' and 'the most original thinker of the sixteenth century'. He might also be dubbed the 'Father of Psychosomatic Medicine', for one of his most fundamental contributions was the recognition of the vital place that the mind, will, imagination, emotions and perception have on the promotion of health and the prevention of disease. 'The power of the imagination is a great factor in medicine,' he wrote. 'It may produce diseases . . . and it may cure them . . . ills of the body may be cured by physical remedies or by the power of the spirit acting through the soul.' Some of his aphorisms, written nearly 500 years ago, have a distinctly modern ring:

> The spirit is the master, the imagination is the instrument, the body is the plastic material.
>     The moral atmosphere surrounding the patient can have a strong influence on the course of his disease.

The church today is endeavouring to revive its healing ministry. In this they would have had the full support of Paracelsus, who believed that virtue was the most potent of all healing forces. He did not decry the use of medicines or surgery, both of which he employed in his own practice, but he felt it vital that doctors should also recognise the spiritual dimension of healing. Physicians must be God-fearing men, he claimed, because medicine was more than a mere collection of facts.

Mary Patterson's life confirmed the validity of this belief. She suffered severe internal injuries in an accident and was pronounced to be in a 'critical' condition. After three days' struggle her doctor decided that there was nothing further he could do to help; so a local minister was called. At this critical point Mary asked for her Bible. Turning by chance to the account of one of Christ's healing miracles – the raising of the palsied man – she slowly scanned the words of hope and inspiration. As she read, she felt the presence and healing power of God flooding through her entire being. Quickly her strength returned, and like the palsied man in the story, she rose from her bed and walked. This episode in February 1866 was a milestone in the history of mental healing, and a turning-point in the life of Mary Patterson, better known as Mary Baker Eddy, the founder of Christian Science. Her moment of inspiration was as abrupt as Newton's discovery of the laws of gravity or Archimedes' realisation of the principles of hydrodynamics. In a flash she realised that where healing is concerned: 'Mind is all and matter is naught.'

Doctors are generally sceptical of reports of spiritual healing; yet well-documented cases exist which should convince even the most bigoted materialist. Every year thousands of pilgrims visit Lourdes. Most who visit the shrine of the Virgin Mary experience a feeling of enhanced well-being. Some report relief or recovery from sickness. But these personal testimonies are not accepted as sufficient proof of spiritual healing by the Official Bureau of Church and State, a body set up to investigate the validity of 'miracle' cures. During the last hundred years the Bureau's team of doctors has carefully scrutinised thousands of cases of remarkable recovery, but has accepted only a few dozen as scientifically unquestionable 'miracles'. To achieve this status the healings must satisfy three main tests: they must occur more rapidly than normal, they must show no signs of relapse over a follow-up period of seven years and they must be accompanied by the complete disappearance of all the clinical features of the disease.

One woman visited Lourdes and experienced what she considered to be a 'miracle' cure. She was suffering from advanced ankylosing spondylitis, a chronic rheumatic disease which had completely fused her spine, making it impossible for her to bend down. This is a crippling deformity for which there is no known medical cure. Yet when the woman was praying at the Grotto her back suddenly regained its full mobility, so that she was able to bend down and pick things off the floor with neither pain nor disability. Functionally there was no doubt of her amazing recovery, but the medical committee could not accept this as evidence of a miracle, as there was no sign of improvement in her X-ray pictures. They were more tolerant in the case of the little boy who developed infective meningitis which left him paralysed and blind. He regained his sight and total mobility after his second immersion in the holy water. This was declared an official miracle. So too was the healing of an emaciated lady who was dying from rectal cancer when she was taken to Lourdes. She had undergone an unsuccessful operation and was in so much agony that she required four injections of morphine a day to ease her pain. After bathing in the water of Lourdes her pain eased and her tumour receded. Within ten months she had regained 36 lb in weight. Years later she remained well with no sign of recurrence of her growth.

Most doctors who have visited Lourdes have been impressed by the healings wrought. Others have pondered over another mystery – which might be called the hidden enigma of Lourdes. Every day hundreds of sick pilgrims bathe in the holy waters. Some are suffering from infectious diseases, others have suppurating wounds. And yet in ninety years there has been no record of cross-infection, such as holiday-makers suffer when swimming in polluted seas or patients acquire when undergoing hospital treatment. Nor has there been any account of an emaciated pilgrim or heart victim suffering from hypothermia after being dipped in the shrine's icy water. 'Here is a phenomenon beyond medical reasoning,' reported one doctor, 'which cannot be explained by science and which is outside the normal laws of hygiene.'

Miracles happen in spiritual settings, but they can equally well occur where the ambience is purely secular. In the 1920s the small French town of Nancy was the seat of one of Europe's least pretentious healing sanctuaries. It was set up by Emil Coué, founder of the school of Auto-suggestive Therapy, who provided daily proof that miracles can be achieved by thought control. By this means he overcame cases which had proved resistant to prolonged medical treatment, such as anaemia, asthma, stammering, varicose ulcers and dyspepsia. Coué's approach to therapy was simple and positive. On one occasion his help was sought by a disabled peasant who had been forced to abandon his work as a blacksmith because for nearly ten years he had been unable to raise his right arm above the horizontal. Coué listened carefully to his story and then assured him that he would be completely cured. 'For ten years you have been thinking that you could not lift your arm above the shoulder,' he explained, 'consequently you have not been able to do so, for whatever we think becomes true for us.' To break the spell, the man was asked to believe that he could raise his arm. The blacksmith looked sceptical. 'Quick,' said Coué in a tone that commanded instant obedience. 'Think "I can, I can!".' The man made a half-hearted attempt to raise his arm, but stopped when he felt a twinge of pain. Coué complimented him on making this modest progress, then urged him to overcome his pain by repeating as quickly as possible the words '*Ça passe, ça passe, ça passe!*' (It is going, it is going, it is going.) For a brief while the man repeated these words while Coué gently stroked his arm. Afterwards he said that his pain had lifted. 'Now think well that you can lift your arms,' instructed Coué. This time, having witnessed the disappearance of his pain, the man had more trust. 'I can,' he said with a mixture of confidence and incredulity, as he slowly raised his arm high above his head. Everyone present applauded his achievement. Coué shook his hand and said: 'My friend you are cured. Now prove it. Hit me on the shoulder.' The man laughed and gave him a gentle tap. 'Hit me harder – as hard as you can.' Gradually the blacksmith entered into the spirit of the occasion and increased the strength of his blows until Coué was forced to ask him to stop. 'There you are, my friend,' he said as he brought the demonstration to a close, 'you can go back to your anvil.'

Cures like these brought Coué world-wide fame, but he remained essentially a modest man and went to great lengths to remind his admirers that throughout his entire life he had never healed a single person. 'Everyone carries the instrument of their own well-being in their brains,' he stressed. 'The function of the therapist is merely to help patients adopt an attitude of healthy-mindedness.' Scientists were forced to concede that Coué's methods worked, although they felt more comfortable when they limited the effectiveness of auto-suggestion to cases with a strong psychosomatic background, like asthma and eczema. But this qualified acceptance did not tally with the actual results achieved at the Nancy clinic, which showed that organic diseases are as amenable to cure by suggestion as functional complaints. This at first sight may seem remarkable, until one remembers that the brain controls *every* function of the human body.

At one time physiologists divided the human nervous system into two completely separate entities – the *central* nervous system and the *autonomic* nervous system. The first acted above the level of consciousness and governed physical sensations and bodily movements. The second regulated the function of the internal organs – heart, blood vessels, glands, stomach, bladder, intestine. This behind-the-scenes network of ganglia and vegetative nerve fibres was judged to lead an existence which was completely autonomous and totally beyond our conscious control. It is now realised that this dichotomy is totally false. If we want, we can control our circulation or the movements of our bowels just as we can blink an eyelid or raise an arm.

Most people would consider that they have little control over the circulation to their hands. But this limitation is self-induced, as has been proved by a series of carefully controlled experiments carried out at the Menninger Foundation, New York, under the direction of Dr Elmer Green and his wife Alyce. One of the Greens' early subjects was Swami Rama, a yoga teacher from India, who demonstrated remarkable control over his circulation.

By an effort of will Swami Rama could make his heart race at 300 beats a minute or check its beating until it made no trace on an electrocardiogram. At other times he would vary the temperature of his hands, making one hand hot and the other hand cold. Such was the fineness of his control that he could even make his thumbs hot and his little fingers cold, producing a temperature drop across the palm of up to eleven degrees Fahrenheit.

But one does not have to be an experienced yogi, or undergo years of esoteric tuition, to master the body's autonomic functions. Even laymen, with no experience or training, can control the circulation to their hands if they apply the right mental approach. This was proved when a professor from a university in Arizona attended a meeting at the Menninger Foundation and accepted an invitation to be a test subject. Without any coaching or advice he was challenged to increase the temperature of his right hand. This he did without too much difficulty, raising the temperature of the hand by seven degrees Fahrenheit in four minutes. He was then offered the far stiffer test of trying to make one hand hot and the other hand cold. For three minutes he struggled with this task without success, then the researchers' needles showed that the right hand was getting appreciably colder than the left. 'What are you doing?' Dr Green asked. The professor laughed and explained what had happened. For three minutes he had tried to cool his *left* hand by imagining that he was going to the fridge, opening the door and placing his hand on the tray of ice cubes. The ruse hadn't worked for a very simple reason. The fridge he used every day at home was hinged on the *left* side. This meant that he always opened the door with his right hand and removed the ice tray with his left. Because of this habitual arrangement his brain had found it difficult to conjure up the exact picture he had visualised. The moment he realised this, he thought instead of handling the ice cubes with his 'free' right hand, and this immediately brought about the required temperature drop!

Experiments like these may seem to be little more than physiological stunts, but in fact they have great physiological significance. They demonstrate that the blood flow to the surface of the body is subject to voluntary control. This means that it

49

should be possible to control circulatory disorders like migraine, high blood pressure and Raynaud's disease (circulatory obstruction). This in fact has proved to be true. In one research project Dr Joseph Sargent, the Menninger Foundation's director of Internal Medicine, took a group of 200 migraine sufferers and taught them how to control the circulation to their heads. An amazing 80 per cent reported beneficial results, ranging from slight to excellent.

This latent power invites a wide variety of practical applications. On a cold day, for instance, we should be able to 'think' ourselves warm. This is done in Tibet, where neophyte monks are trained to engender bodily heat by a process of visualisation. In this art, known as *tumo*, they are taught to picture miniature suns resting on their hands and feet and flooding their whole body with warmth. Once they master this practice they are given a proficiency test, which in some ways is very similar to the initiation rites undertaken by tenderfoot Red Indians. On a winter's day they are made to sit in sheets dipped in ice-cold lake water. These they have to dry with the heat of their body. Those who succeed in drying three sheets in a row are given the title *reapa* or 'cotton-clad one'.

Laboratory tests have also shown that we can regulate the movement of our bowels, another function which was previously thought to be completely beyond our conscious control. (This will come as little surprise to mothers, who generally find that children can be trained to dispense with nappies after two or three years!) It is a matter of everyday observation that the gut responds to emotional stimulation. We get 'butterflies' in the stomach when we are nervous, feel 'sickened' when we are disappointed, suffer cramping pains when we 'bellyache' about a neighbour's misdemeanours and experience an urgent desire to defecate when we are beset with sudden fear. Even the mere fact of discussing unpleasant topics has been shown to increase the pressure within the colons of many healthy individuals, a reaction which can be strong enough to produce pain and to aggravate the functional inadequacies of patients suffering from irritable colons and functional diarrhoea.

This distress can be relieved by drugs which ease the intestinal spasm, or by biofeedback training which enables patients to control the intensity of their bowel movements in a way which is both natural and free of adverse side-effects. Many people suffer from functional diarrhoea, a frequent emptying of the bowels for which there is no detectable pathological cause. Trials show that these unfortunate people need not be left the helpless victims of fate, or the constant recipients of medical aid, but can be taught to gain a degree of conscious control of their hyperactive bowel movements. This is achieved by placing an electronic stethoscope over their bellies and wiring it to a loudspeaker capable of amplifying the sound of even the smallest contraction of the bowel muscles. Given this feedback, they can relax on a reclining chair and practise making their bowels quieter or noisier. This enables the intestines to be brought under partial voluntary control in a remarkably short time. In one trial five sufferers, all house-bound because of their incontinence, gained a worthwhile degree of mastery over their bowels in just five, half-hour training sessions.

The human brain's versatility can also exercise control over cellular growth. Most doctors can cite well-authenticated cases of warts which have been charmed away by hypnosis, auto-suggestion, faith-healing or placebo folk cures. My favourite incident involved a patient who was herself a famous faith-healer, but who found it exceedingly difficult to cure her own ailments. She was merely a vessel through which the healing force flowed, she explained, and as such she could not direct the power towards herself. I had helped her recover from tension headaches, strained knees and acute back pains, but my particular treatment could not assist her when her hand developed a crop of unsightly warts. So she decided to visit 'Tom', a farm labourer who had gained a reputation as an adept wart charmer and who lived some seventy miles from her London home. She eventually tracked him down in his favourite haunt – the village pub – and told him her problem. 'Count the number of your warts,' he said, 'and give me one copper coin for every wart.' She looked down at her right hand and counted five large warts. As the man flatly refused to take any further payment for his services, not even a pint of beer, she simply gave him five pennies from her purse and left the pub. In seven times seven days, she was told, the warts would be gone. This proved to be an accurate prediction, for after a month or so the warts began to disappear. By the end of the forty-nine days only one growth remained. This was a small wart on her *left* hand, which had not been included in the original reckoning and so had escaped the healing ministrations of her mind!

A more impressive case of mental healing occupied the attention of the British medical fraternity in 1952. This concerned a case, fully documented in the *British Medical Journal*, of a sixteen-year-old lad who was suffering from an incurable skin complaint known as *ichthyosiform erythrodermia*. Practically the whole of the boy's body was covered with an unsightly, thick, black horny layer which had more in common with a reptile's shell than smooth human skin. Here and there the ugly carapace was fissured and infected. Blood and serum oozed through the cracks. The young-ster had been taken into hospital for numerous treatments, but none had proved effective. Gradually he was withdrawing more and more from the company of his friends, for the sight and smell of his encrusted armour plating made him a social outcast. Eventually he went to Britain's premier plastic surgery unit, which was under the control of Sir Archibald McIndoe, the surgeon who had done so much to restore the shattered faces of RAF pilots injured during the Battle of Britain. This was his last hope. Maybe his blackened carcass could be removed patch by patch and replaced by healthy tissue. When this approach failed one of the surgical team had a bright idea. Dr Albert Mason had been the anaesthetist at both of the boy's plastic surgery operations. He also happened to be a skilled hypnotist. In the past he had removed warts by using post-hypnotic suggestion. Why should not the same technique be effective in this case, which seemed to be no more than a gross case of warts? His colleagues dismissed the suggestion with contempt. But Mason was not deterred and decided to put his notion to the test. So he hypnotised the young man and told him that the warts would fall off his left arm. 'About five days later the horny layer softened, became friable, and fell off,' Mason reported in the *British Medical Journal*. The healing process continued and after another five days the left arm was 'completely clear from shoulder to wrist'. Subsequent treatment cleared the right arm and secured a 50 per cent improvement in the condition of the legs and feet. Although his skin was not completely normal the boy was physically and mentally a changed person. Because of his progress he was able to take a job and became 'a normal, happy boy'.

Mason's colleagues were astounded by the results. 'Do you know what you've done?' the team's senior surgeon said. This wasn't a matter of simple wart charming. 'This is a case of congenital *ichthyosiform erythrodermia,*' the surgeon emphasised. 'Now go into the library and look it up.' Mason did so, and for the first time he realised the gravity of the boy's condition, which had been recognised since 1902 as a congenital, progressive and incurable disease. Medicine was powerless to halt its progress, but the healing power of the mind was able to bring rapid relief the moment it was effectively harnessed. This is a reality which many doctors still find difficult to accept. 'For something like this to change,' said one specialist, 'is really as unbelievable as for a club foot to change.'

But thoughts and mental attitudes *can* heal – sometimes even the most chronic, life-threatening conditions. Unfortunately thoughts can also maim, for as Hamlet said: 'There is nothing either good or bad but thinking makes it so.' Every day doctors see scores of self-made invalids. Sometimes they call their problem functional overlay or organ neurosis; at other times, for obvious reasons, they label the condition 'the fat file syndrome'. At one time the constantly complaining female patient was judged to be suffering from 'hysteria', since her endless sequence of symptoms was thought to stem from disorders of the womb. Another explanation had to be found for the permanently sick male. Since he did not have a womb, it was suggested that *his* symptoms originated under the rib cage or *hypochondrium* – hence the term *hypochondriasis.*

Many people lead lives of quiet desperation because of their morbid preoccupations. Samuel Johnson, the great author and lexicographer, admitted that hypochondria was the most deplorable element of his character. He enjoyed continual illness throughout his life and even took the precaution of inviting a doctor to share his London home so he could have daily access to medical treatment. Although he was an extremely hospitable man, Dr Johnson gave short shrift to fellow moaners. One of his visitors invariably launched into a non-stop organ recital, generally about the unhappy state of his innards. 'Do not be like the spider, man, and spin conversation thus incessantly out of thine own bowels,' said Johnson. Some people try to take a flippant or familiar attitude towards their morbid mental states. Abraham Lincoln, made a friend of his *hypochondriasis*, which he called 'the hypo'. Others joke about their neurotic obsessions: like the film star who admitted that he took so many antibiotics that whenever he sneezed everyone around him got cured! But mental morbidity is no laughing matter. One survey, carried out among a selection of middle-aged Minnesota business and professional men, showed that the hypochondriacs within the group had an increased risk of developing coronary disease, even though they were clinically healthy initially apart from their negative outlook.

If we care for our health and happiness we should no more entertain morbid thoughts than drink polluted water or eat contaminated food. It is right to show proper concern for the sickness of our fellow beings, but reckless and irresponsible to encourage them in the frivolous discussion of trivial aches and pains. You would not share a person's dirty handkerchief, so why be willing to share their infected thoughts?

Hypochondriacs and depressives are health hazards, capable of transmitting their sickness to everyone with whom they come into contact, as surely as sufferers from smallpox or AIDS. Doctors are frequently infected with the negative thoughts of their patients, which may be why so many of them suffer stress ailments, 'burn-out', heart disease and nervous breakdown. The risk of suffering mental contamination is even greater for psychiatrists, hence no doubt their exceptionally poor record of mental health and their high risk of suicide.

We may not be able to choose our genes, but we can order our thoughts. Each moment we have a choice: whether we think positive, life-enhancing thoughts, or dwell on negative and destructive concepts and images. Each day we make our own bed, out of a mattress stuffed with the fabric of our thoughts and dreams. On this we have to lie. For the hypochondriac it will be a bed of sickness, since this is the only roost their minds can fashion. For the optimist it will be a bed of roses. The difference is vast, and yet it can be achieved by a relatively slight modification of life-style, as succeeding chapters will show.

Chapter Five:

# THE THERAPY WITHIN

People today are growing increasingly dissatisfied with high-tech medicine which, like an electioneering politician, seems to promise much but deliver little. The nations of the civilised world are spending a phenomenal sum on medical care, and yet their citizens report a steady decline in health standards. This was highlighted in a recent report by Professor Jeffrey Bland published in the *New England Journal of Medicine*. Entitled 'The Paradox of Health', Professor Bland's paper revealed that Americans in the 1920s reported suffering an average of less than one episode of disabling illness per year. By the early 1980s this figure had risen to over two episodes of invalidism a year. Yet during these years the total US expenditure on health care had increased exponentially, rising from $75 billion in 1970 to a colossal $456 billion in 1986. Therein lies the nub of the paradox: that health standards have declined and sickness flourished during a period which has witnessed an unprecedented expansion of medical technology and a vast growth in health expenditure. Despite an enormous outlay on medical care we are not creating healthier or happier citizens, merely nations which are better cared for when sickness strikes.

There is a widespread feeling that twentieth-century medicine has let us down, a disappointment that has encouraged many people to switch their allegiance to alternative methods of healing, such as homeopathy, herbal medicine, reflexology and acupuncture. But these fringe practices are unlikely to usher in the new millennium of health. Acupuncture may be highly effective in easing neuralgic pain, and herbal analgesics like willow bark may ease the pain of lumbago but these complementary medical practices cannot be expected to produce a major shift in health care. However many clinics of natural medicine are established, we will still be faced with hordes of people whom medicine – orthodox or otherwise – cannot cure. And masses of our fellows will continue to inhabit the sad, grey, limbo land called Disease. This largely uncharted but densely populated territory is reserved for the rejects of modern medical practice; men, women and children who do not suffer from any recognisable disease process but who are nevertheless well aware that they are not enjoying vibrant health. These are the 'vertically ill' who drag themselves about in a constant state of sub-health. Sir James Watt, past President of the Royal Society of Medicine, accepts the estimate 'that one-third of patients with chronic symptoms have no organic disease and that another third exhibit symptoms unrelated to their organic condition'. These patients are suffering from what is often termed 'undifferentiated illness', which surgeon Michael Baum of King's College School of Medicine describes as 'a special malaise requiring an infusion of spiritual solace'.

At some time we must accept that our modern approach to health care has failed. This realisation will come when we acknowledge that health is very often an attitude of mind and an expression of an individually chosen life-style. Where our personal health is concerned, we are our own best physicians. The widespread acceptance of this simple fact can bring about a new era of health care. This is the true 'alternative' medicine of the future.

Every one of us is a walking pharmacy and ambulant hospital. When we are sick we rarely need to rely on outside medical aid, for our bodies contain all the drugs and therapeutic processes necessary to ease pain, heal wounds, repair broken bones, destroy malignant growths, conquer allergies, cure insomnia, overcome hypertension, alleviate depression and assuage anxiety. When we cut a finger the body's corps of nursing orderlies swings immediately into action, staunching the bleeding and laying down a fibrin clot to heal the wound. This miracle of tissue repair is carried out without our conscious thought or active intervention. We may choose to cleanse and dress the wound, or draw its gaping edges together with a row of sutures, but these activities are peripheral to the basic healing process. Operations today can be marvels of technical sophistication and physical dexterity. With an amalgam of human skill and scientific hardware, surgeons can exchange defective heart valves and insert artificial knee joints – but they remain powerless to heal even the small cut. Ambroise Paré was Renaissance Europe's greatest surgeon. Acclaimed as the doctor who treated a succession of four French kings, and who revolutionised the craft of surgery with his dazzling new techniques and instruments, he was nevertheless humble enough to recognise his utter dependence on the healing power of Nature. When he was praised for saving the life of a wounded soldier, he replied: 'I dressed him, but God healed him.'

What is true of wound repair is equally true of the combat of infection, or the eradication of foreign bodies. If we develop tonsillitis the throat becomes inflamed, not because it is diseased, but because the area quickly becomes a battlefield flooded with blood carrying a high titre of infection-combating leucocytes (white blood cells). When food lodges in our windpipe we cough. When grit gets in an eye we shed a copious flow of tears to wash away the irritating particle. These are all examples of the body's inherent tendency to heal itself, which are so commonplace that we often take them for granted. Yet human life could not be maintained without this all-powerful, all-pervasive *vis medicatrix naturae*.

The scientific discoveries of recent years, far from exposing the mysteries of human existence, have merely given us further cause for wonder. In the course of this research far more has been learnt about the body's internal pharmacy. We now know that our systems manufacture substances to alleviate pain – known as endorphins since they are manufactured within the body and mimic the action of morphine (*endogenous morphines*). Other studies have revealed the existence of a group of naturally occurring peptides (amino-acid compounds), sometimes referred to as 'antineoplastons', which are capable of checking the growth of cancer cells. Earlier investigations revealed that the body also manufactures a neuropeptide called serotonin, which helps to prevent the onset of depression. This discovery led directly to the development of a range of anti-depressant drugs known as the monoamine oxidase inhibitors, which owe their effectiveness to their ability to build up the levels of serotonin within the brain.

One of the basic principles of Andrew Taylor Still, the founder of osteopathy, was that all the pharmaceutical agents required for the maintenance of health are manufactured within the human body. The recent discoveries of the infant science of neuroendocrinology have made this claim seem a little less audacious than it was when first propounded. We now have proof that the body produces chemicals capable of overcoming chronic insomnia, for conquering cancer, deadening pain or lifting the 'black dog' of despair. Just as we can utilise a word processor without understanding the intricacies of computer technology, so we can harness these resources without understanding the intimate details of human biochemistry. Wherever we live and whatever our financial situation, we can all call on the counsel of the finest physician the world has ever known – the human brain. Within our minds – whatever our experience, intelligence or level of medical education – we have a tool which is admirably equipped to foster health and frustrate disease.

Lone voices in the past – like Mesmer, Coué and Mary Baker Eddy – have urged us to put our trust in the healing power of human thought. The great tragedy of twentieth-century medicine is that we have resisted their enlightened call. Rather than rely on our own, God-given faculties, we have chosen to put our faith in the potions and healing rites of medical scientists. These are the gurus on whom we rely for our happiness and health. Over the years we have accepted their creed of 'a pill for every ill'. Instead of depending on the inherent regulating powers of the body, we have been cajoled into taking laxatives to move our bowels, sedatives to make us sleep, stimulants to keep us awake, expectorants to make us cough and anti-histamines to check our sniffles. Even more insidious has been our growing dependence on 'happiness pills'. When Aldous Huxley wrote his fantasy *Brave New World* he looked forward to the time when man would develop a ubiquitous drug – called Soma – which would promote universal happiness by providing a safe and easily available escape from the tensions and anxieties of everyday life. Many people thought that Huxley's chemical utopia had arrived when the pharmaceutical industry developed the minor tranquillisers Librium and Valium. These chemical dummies were hailed with great enthusiasm, and were widely used until it was realised that they often provoked adverse side-effects and gave rise to problems of addiction in a third to a half of patients treated.

With the growth of the pharmaceutical industry, we have medicalised many of our social and spiritual problems. Today we expect to be offered a sedative drug when we are bereaved. When we have a row with a next-door neighbour we take tranquillisers, preferring medication to reconciliation. When we become aware of the futility of our lives, we do not set out to nourish our souls, but turn instead to anti-depressant medication. But pills cannot solve our personal problems. Drugs cannot change gloom into joy, or turn depression to euphoria.

As patients we have been grossly unfair to the medical profession, in expecting them to meet these unreasonable demands. We have asked our doctors to become magicians rather than medical scientists. The pen with which they write their prescriptions has become for us a conjuror's wand. We go to them with our problems and pains, just as we once went to mummy asking her to 'kiss us better'. This extension of medical practice has caused a widespread overprescription of drugs. According to an estimate made some while ago by Professor T. Higuchi, Regents Professor of Pharmaceutical Chemistry at Kansas University, approximately 90 per cent of drugs administered today are unnecessary.

This wholesale abuse of chemotherapy has led to a vast

explosion of iatrogenic disease – the ailments directly caused by modern medication – which some doctors estimate as being responsible for up to 30 per cent of today's illness. In Britain 40 per cent of admissions to geriatric hospitals are due to iatrogenic disease. In some cases these elderly patients are literally 'cured to death'. Medical historians in years to come will no doubt wonder at the scale of our present drug dependence, and may with good reason dub the period in which we are living the Great Stoned Age.

Iatrogenic disease can disfigure, maim and kill; but the main adverse effect of our current pharmaceutical drug dependency is that it takes away our sense of personal responsibility. A businessman may be unable to sleep because he has financial worries. In desperation he visits his doctor who prescribes sleeping pills. This crutch may alleviate his insomnia but cannot conceivably reduce his overdraft. A housewife suffers 'nerves' while going through a period of marital strife. She takes Valium, supported by hefty slugs of gin and tonic. This masks her disquiet, but does nothing to restore domestic bliss. A church worker is unwittingly embroiled in a tax fiddle at his office which troubles his conscience. For weeks he feels as if he is carrying a heavy burden on his shoulders. In time the responsibility and strain combine to give him a tension headache. He doses himself with aspirin, which eases the pain but does not resolve his ethical dilemma.

In all these instances the body presents uncomfortable symptoms as a warning that something is amiss and requires remedial action. To suppress the symptoms without taking the necessary corrective measures merely prolongs the unsatisfactory situation. Sometimes the condition is aggravated by taking drugs. The sedative pills the businessman takes may make him uncomfortably drowsy during the day and so less able to overcome his financial predicament. The tranquillisers which the unhappy housewife swallows can make her unusually belligerent by suppressing her normal inhibitions. If so her domestic problems may be intensified rather than relieved. A satisfactory solution to cases like these can never be found in a bottle of pills.

It is customary to regard sickness as an unmitigated tragedy.

But it also provides an excellent opportunity for change. When a smoker gets a cough he is more likely to find the resolve to give up cigarettes. When a dyspeptic suffers a gastric ulcer he is encouraged to eat more sensibly. Heart attacks inspire sedentary businessmen to take more exercise, and nervous breakdowns provide the ideal incentive for workaholics to take life more easily. So it should be when we suffer the often undifferentiated illnesses of the mind. If we wish for no more than a temporary solution to our problems we can suppress our symptoms with drugs, or we can take grateful account of the warning signs and seek to make a permanent improvement in our health and mental outlook.

For generations enlightened physicians have been issuing a warning against indiscriminate pill-taking. Sir William Osler was well aware of man's unquestioning allegiance to, and obsessive desire for, folk remedies and patent medicines: 'The desire to take medicines is perhaps the greatest feature which distinguishes man from animals,' he said. Somehow this dependence must be broken, particularly today when the adverse effects of powerful drugs like Thalidomide and Opren are infinitely more serious than the diseases they aim to cure. This must become a prime task of health educationalists in the future. As Osler said: 'One of the prime duties of the physician is to educate the masses not to take drugs.' But what help will doctors give their patients if they deprive them of their customary drug potions and pills? Will they be left to solve their own problems, or will they be given guidance in fundamental life skills? The word 'doctor' derives from the Latin verb *docere*, and originally meant a teacher. Is it too much to hope that physicians in future will revert to this earlier role, and once again take up the mantle of men of wisdom and learning, whose function is to educate the mind and heal the soul as well as doctor the body?

The evidence presented in earlier chapters of this book suggests that the dispersion of spiritual wisdom could do more to relieve mental suffering and psychosomatic illness than the dispensation of medical drugs. People suffering from psychiatric illness are encouraged today to take psychotropic medicines, but they would almost certainly derive more benefit by reading any of the ancient books of religious teaching and wisdom: the Bible, the teachings of Buddha, the sayings of Confucius, the Koran, the Talmud, the Upanishads. This was the experience of Philippe Pinet, the enlightened eighteenth-century French doctor, who did so much to advance the treatment of mental illness. It was Pinet who boldly removed the chains which bound 'insane' people and who insisted that the mentally ill should be treated as patients rather than criminals. For the first time he introduced humane techniques into the Biçetre Hospital in Paris and as a result discovered that 'the writings of Plato, Seneca and other writers of antiquity were found to be more eminent service in the prevention of insanity than any pharmaceutical formulae'.

We are just beginning to accept that the mind can heal conditions as life-threatening and diverse as heart attacks, cancer and hypertension. This is a major conceptual advance. What we have still to appreciate is the vital role that the brain plays in prophylaxis. It is the fundamental thesis of this book that **a healthy attitude of mind is the single most important factor in the maintenance of health and the prevention of disease**. What this means in practical terms is elaborated in the chapter which follows.

Chapter Six:

# A HOUSEHOLD PHILOSOPHY

Sickness has always been attributed to outside influences. When our forebears were ill they considered themselves to be the innocent victims of extraneous forces, such as pestilence, poisons, sorcery or even an unfortunate conjunction of the stars. It is now less easy to place the blame on scapegoats such as these. Surveys show that much of the sickness we suffer today is of our own making. We are ill – not because we are the hapless targets of noxious outside influences – but because we have chosen to adopt an unhealthy way of life.

This shift of responsibility has changed the direction of health promotion. Sickness, we are constantly being reminded, is the result of life-style indiscretions. Like the revivalist preachers of old, our modern health educators seem more keen to frighten us to death than waken us to life.

This constant assault is producing a generation of educated neurotics, who are becoming afraid to eat for fear of swallowing an overdose of anti-oxidants and scared to breathe in case they inhale a lethal quantity of carbon monoxide. Some see the hobgoblins of illness wherever they turn and make their lives a constant misery by shunning tap water because of its fluoride content, digital watches because of the radiation they emit and aluminium cooking utensils because of the metal contamination they might cause. To such highly imaginative individuals the concealed menaces of the twentieth-century environment – pesticides, food additives, radiation, gas fumes, lead poisoning – are every bit as terrifying as the witches and demons which haunted our predecessors.

Even the most sanguine individuals today are likely to be dismayed by the plethora of health warnings, which confuse, conflict and confound. 'Smoking damages the lungs, alcohol rots the liver, butter clogs the arteries. Too much sex makes you mad, and no sex at all makes you even madder', was one observer's wry summary of the doleful situation. His jaundiced outlook is easily understood, for we have been encouraged to make a penance of getting fit. The healthy life has been portrayed as a joyless, self-denying pilgrimage. Diets have become increasingly dull and unpalatable, a tasteless mixture of bone-meal and bran. 'If it tastes good, spit it out', is a common injunction. The same ascetic approach applies to aerobic exercise where we have been goaded to 'feel the burn'. Playing games for fun finds no place in this Spartan curriculum, where the watchword is 'No pain, no gain'.

The physical fitness movement has served a valuable purpose, even if it has created an unhealthy number of neurotic, introspective hypochondriacal health addicts, food faddists and fitness freaks. But its chief failing is that it has blinded us to the importance of the mind in the promotion of health and the prevention of disease. In recent years this tunnel vision has blinkered the outlook of doctors and laymen alike. The majority of health professionals recognise that personality factors play an important role in the aetiology of high blood pressure and heart disease, but how many make practical application of this knowledge in their daily treatment? Physicians will prescribe beta-blockers, diuretics and anti-hypertensive medicines, but how many will advocate personality counselling? In the same way the medical profession is tentatively prepared to accept that adverse emotional states can predispose to cancer, but has still not grasped the nettle and turned this discovery to prophylactic use.

If it had, it would by now be giving the same enthusiastic backing to personality counselling as it has in the past to campaigns aimed at stopping smoking or preventing alcohol abuse.

The lay public has shown a great willingness to abide by the laws of physical hygiene even when this has involved considerable personal sacrifice. The cult pursuits undertaken have served their purpose. We are now on the threshold of a major advance in health promotion, a breakthrough which will enable us to lead lives of abundant peace, joy, vitality and health. This advance can be attained only by making a change in mental outlook.

My original 'messianic' belief in the value of physical cures was replaced by the recognition that many of my patients were suffering from psychosomatic ailments. Their presenting symptoms might be physical – backache, fibrositis or head pain – but their underlying problems were emotional or stress-related. If I was to help them they needed not only manipulation but also some form of psychotherapeutic guidance. So I developed an interest in psychotherapy and adopted a more holistic approach to health. But the major change in attitude came much later. Throughout my career my twin specialities have been the management of sports injuries and the treatment of elderly people. These interests have provided me with some of my major challenges and keenest rewards. They have also, as it happens, provided me with several important insights. My athlete patients have taught me that physical fitness alone is not enough to ensure a healthy life. In fact I have often been amazed at the poor health records of many world-famous sports stars. These highly trained gladiators seem to be in superlative condition, well-muscled, agile, powerful and spare. In their public appearances they appear to be paragons of physical perfection as they run their sub-four-minute miles and vault their seven-foot high jump bars. Only their doctors know that behind this public façade there often lies an individual troubled with anxieties and doubts and plagued with petty ailments – chronic fatigue, sore throats, catarrh and recurrent crops of boils. Some die young. Some develop arthritic problems as a direct result of the strains they have suffered during their brief athletic careers. Others succumb to what has been called 'athlete's neurosis'. This is a sporting version of the mid-life crisis, a depression triggered off by a sudden loss of identity and self-esteem. The malaise arises when a person makes athletic prowess their sole *raison d'être*. One day they may be Joe Doe, the world-famous hurdler, whose whole life is devoted to the pursuit of physical excellence. The next week they have a hamstring injury which abruptly terminates their career, and overnight they become Joe Who?, the ex-athlete on the slippery downward slope to purposeless anonymity. Experiences like these have convinced me that long-term health and happiness is not to be found by slavish devotion to exercise and dieting.

This contrasts with the cheerful, positive and outgoing outlook of my outstandingly vigorous elderly patients. They invariably prefer a belly-laugh to a bellyache. Most have the ability to laugh at themselves and their infirmities, like the octogenarian politician who said: 'They tell me I'm losing my brain – but I don't miss it.' Mr John Evans of Swansea, who recently held the title of Britain's oldest citizen, showed a similar sense of playfulness when he was taken on his first trip to London at the age of 110. The organisers of his special birthday treat thoughtfully provided him with a wheelchair in case he got tired on his whirlwind tour. But the veteran coal miner protested. 'People will think I am getting old,' he said with a smile. He caused further amusement when he quipped to reporters at the start of his train journey: 'I'm glad to see they've given me a return ticket.'

A sense of fun is undoubtedly one of the qualities which contributes to a healthy philosophy of life.

Doctors working in other specialities have pinpointed further cardinal features of the healthy life philosophy. Unfortunately they have generally chosen to emphasise the negative emotional attitudes which predispose to sickness, rather than highlight the positive mental qualities which predispose to health. Dermatologists have noted that skin diseases are prevalent in patients who harbour feelings of resentment, self-pity, frustration, anxiety, guilt and self-loathing. For years we may suppress our negative emotions, but eventually they erupt like suppurating boils and find release in physical symptoms. Depending on our inherent weaknesses and predispositions, this conversion of nervous energy can give rise to psychosomatic skin diseases, headaches, bowel disorders, rheumatism, heart attacks or cancer. People who are habitually irritated by emotional problems which they allow to 'get under their skin', may finish up with problems which eventually erupt as irritating lesions on the surface of their bodies.

Cardiologists, like Dr Meyer Friedman and Dr Ray Rosenman, have demonstrated that heart attacks are particularly common in individuals who are aggressive, competitive and obsessed with time. As a result of these exhausting drives they 'put their heart' into their daily work, sometimes with disastrous consequences. Gastro-enterologists have observed a similar link between emotional attitudes and diseases of the intestine and stomach. Peptic ulcers are often found to be associated with anxiety or repressed hostility. This relationship was clearly shown by the personal experience of a Chicago gastro-enterologist who took regular daily analyses of the contents of his own stomach for experimental purposes. After taking 3,000 of these recordings he was involved in a tragedy in which his home was invaded by burglars who shot and killed his landlady. The doctor was the only eyewitness who could identify the villains. His vital evidence led to their eventual arrest, but for ten days he was fearful that he might be the victim of gang reprisals. During this period he carried on doing his daily experiments, and found that the acidity of his gastric contents had doubled. Prolonged anxiety states are obviously harmful for the stomach, as they are for other organs of the body.

Cancer specialists have made further contributions to the delineation of the ideal mental attitude. Clinical psychotherapist Dr Lawrence LeShan analysed the life histories of more than 500 cancer patients. His investigation, described in *You Can Fight for Your Life*, revealed a close link between depression and despair and the onset of cancer. Many patients had felt defeated by breakdowns in intensely close personal relationships, emotional set-backs which they did their utmost to conceal. As a result they went through life harbouring feelings of suppressed despair, a mood which altered their neurohormonal balance and probably had an adverse effect upon their immune response.

Similar studies carried out by other medical researchers have supported the accuracy of LeShan's observation. Dr A. H. Schmale and Dr H. Iker of the University of Rochester, New York confined their attention to a study of female patients with cervical cancer. They found that these unfortunate women commonly experienced frustration and despair over emotional conflicts which they felt powerless to resolve. Using psychological measures they could identify these 'helplessness-prone personalities' in advance. In this way they were able to take a group of healthy women with a biological predisposition to cervical cancer, and predict with 72.5 per cent accuracy the women who would eventually develop malignant growths.

Everyone has fleeting moments when they feel angry, helpless, anxious, despondent, miserable, resentful or frustrated. The occasional experience of these negative feelings is both natural and healthy, since it alerts us to defects in our emotional environment and motivates us to make whatever life-style changes are necessary to restore our psychic health and physical well-being. Problems arise only when these passing emotions persist and become transformed into permanent moods. When this happens, gastric ulcers may develop as a result of long-continued states of frustrated hostility, or heart attacks strike because of attitudes of unrelieved aggression.

Attitudes of mind are important determinants of health and equally crucial determinants of longevity. The way we think and feel conditions the *quality* of our lives, and often controls its *quantity* as well. This was demonstrated by a prospective study of over 200 men, carried out by a Harvard research team. The men were chosen because they shared a similar academic background, social status and financial standing. All were in their forties at the start of the survey and enjoyed good health. A decade later twenty of the men were dead, long before they reached retirement age. But the deaths did not strike at random. Tests showed that only 3 per cent of the emotionally healthy men had died by the age of fifty-three; whereas 38 per cent of the men with the lowest mental health ratings were either dead or chronically ill at this early age.

Psychologists have extended this line of research and in the process have given us a clearer picture still of the emotional attitudes which promote health and enhance life. Few contributions in this field have been greater than that of the late Abraham Maslow, past-President of the American Psychological Association, who was one of the most original thinkers in the human potential movement. He started out by making a character analysis of two remarkable human beings, his teachers Max Wertheimer and Ruth Benedict. He considered them to be admirable examples of successful, well-adjusted individuals, and wanted to see what made them tick. When he studied his notes he found, to his surprise and delight, that they shared certain qualities and values. 'I was talking about a kind of person,' he later recalled, 'not about two non-comparable individuals.' Armed with this finding he extended his study to a wider range of enviable individuals. Unlike his colleagues, who spent their lives studying the mentally ill and misfits of society, Maslow thought it would be more revealing if he studied the lives of people who were outstandingly healthy, competent and contented. Once again he found that these outstanding individuals, whatever their different occupations and physical life-styles, shared certain important mental characteristics. All were committed to a task or cause which gave them a strong sense of motivation and purpose. All had a clear-cut idea of their own identity and were able to make independent value judgements without being unduly influenced by the opinions and beliefs of others. They were autonomous and self-reliant and yet they related easily with their families, colleagues and friends. In addition Maslow found that these 'self-actualising' individuals were spontaneous rather than rigid, and serene rather than anxious. As a result of his research he had identified a syndrome of healthy-mindedness – a cluster of emotional qualities which acted together synergistically to promote contentment, health, happy relationships and the successful attainment of lifetime goals and aspirations.

Maslow's discoveries were heralded as a major psychological revelation when they were first published. Yet they merely echoed, and gave scientific credence to, doctrines which had been taught by generations of philosophers and religious teachers. For centuries priests have used invocations to banish mental woes and physical ills. One of the twin aims of these healing prayers has been to exorcise the negative emotions which contribute to sickness. Their other goal has been to encourage the reparative emotions which foster health. So we have prayers which banish the anxieties which stem from guilt; others which seek to overcome doubt, self-pity, insecurity and bitterness. On the positive side we find prayers which ask for the benison of Maslow's constellation of life-enhancing attitudes – cheerfulness, patience, calm, serenity, forgiveness, acceptance, an untroubled mind and a peaceful, loving heart.

Philosophy has been another medium by which people have developed a wholesome mental attitude. This was especially true in the great Graeco-Roman age, when men like Socrates, Plato, Epictetus, Antisthenes and Plotinus mingled with the people and discussed with them the practical issues of daily living – love, death, duty, morals, justice and honour. Philosophy then was a guide to everyday living, rather than a remote, academic discipline. In Athens and Rome the peripatetic philosopher was as conspicuous as the market trader today. Leading a simple life, going about barefoot like Socrates or living in a barrel like Diogenes, they conducted their dialogues in the city squares, street corners, public baths and gladiatorial sports arenas. They taught principles which the average man could understand and emulate. Not so their successors today, the nameless men who cloister themselves in remote, university chambers and speak an esoteric language which only the intellectually enlightened can understand.

Societies do not bestow their honours indiscriminately. When we give our rewards today to doctors, scientists, business tycoons, inventors, TV entertainers and pop musicians, it is because we believe that they are making an important contribution to the weal of human health and happiness. If philosophy wants to regain the exalted position it held in the days of Plato and Socrates, it will have to make a contribution as relevant and purposeful as that supplied by those great public teachers.

We do not need a philosophy which proves or disproves the fact of human existence. Most people are sufficiently reassured that they exist when they get out of bed every morning and face themselves in the bathroom mirror. What we urgently require is a practical philosophy of life which enables us to lead a more richly fulfilling existence; which guides us through periods of adversity; which fosters happiness and health and which spreads concord and peace throughout the world.

Such a blueprint for everyday living is far too important to remain the exclusive domain of a remote handful of academic philosophers. This household *Weltanschauung* should constitute the very core of folk wisdom and provide the golden thread of childhood training. These behavioural guidelines should be promulgated on television, preached from the pulpit, discussed in the pub and taught in doctors' surgeries. These are the principles which can revolutionise our lives. Bruno Bettelheim, the distinguished German psychoanalyst, spent a year in the concentration camps of Dachau and Buchenwald. This gave him remarkable insights into the ways people respond to adversity. Some survived with their bodies broken but their spirits intact. Others suffered a rapid breakdown in their personalities and their will to live. What characterised the casualties of this brutalising process? According to Bettelheim: 'they had no consistent philosophy that would protect their integrity as human beings.' It was not a want of intelligence or physical fitness that caused their downfall, but a lack of a dominant system of beliefs. It is at times like these that we put our philosophies to the test, as Admiral Richard Byrd found when he made his famous trek to the South Pole. In his book *Alone* he describes the mental strain his men suffered during their long confinement in the ice-bound waste-land of Antarctica. At times like these, he wrote, 'men are driven deeper and deeper into themselves for materials of replenish-ment. And on these hidden levels of self-replenishment, which might be called the pay levels of philosophy, would depend the ability of any group of men to outlast such an ordeal and not come to hate each other.' We may not be condemned to life in a concentration camp, nor are we likely to join a polar expedition, but during our lives we will inevitably suffer emotional traumas and threats to our self-esteem and individuality. How we respond to these assaults will depend to a large extent on our personal *Weltanschauung*. How this life-promoting philosophy can be acquired and strengthened is described in the chapter which follows.

# Chapter Seven:

---

# PROGRAMMED FOR HEALTH

---

In our current search for health we are becoming increasingly analytical and introspective. Instead of relishing our meals we count their calorie-content. At the end of a vigorous game of tennis, instead of relaxing and enjoying the post-match glow, we check our cardiac fitness by measuring our pulse recovery rate. In the process our lives are becoming scientifically calculated performances rather than expressions of spontaneous delight.

This is equally true of our personal relationships. Years of psychoanalytical theorising have encouraged us to unravel the warp and weft of our intimate encounters, which can leave our emotional lives threadbare and tangled. When we suffer a passing slight we wonder whether our feelings of inadequacy stem from a lack of parental love. While we struggle with this largely academic question life goes on – without us. When we fall madly in love, instead of enjoying the passionate abandonment of the moment, we start to intellectualise, and wonder if the object of our delight is loving us, not for ourselves, but for our money, or because we represent a father figure or mother substitute.

This constant introspection is generating sickness rather than health. Human existence is too short to be frittered away in idle conjecture. If we insist on understanding and justifying every step we take – each morsel of food we eat, each non-verbal gesture we make – we will end up thinking much but doing little. It would require several well-stocked medical libraries to house even a fraction of our contemporary knowledge of human physiology. No one person today can acquire this vast compendium of knowledge. How then can they expect to lead textbook lives?

Anyone who attempts to subject every facet of their lives to scientific scrutiny is doomed to frustration and failure; a shortfall which will grow increasingly pronounced as our medical knowledge expands. What then is the alternative? How should we organise our daily lives to optimise our health and happiness, if not by the process of rational and deliberate choice?

The answer lies, as it always has, in the establishment of sensible behavioural habits. We have neither the time, the knowledge, nor the need to analyse every action we take. A child may take an age to put on a shirt or blouse, but by the time we reach adulthood we have established a set routine which makes this action second nature. We do not stop to think which sleeve should be filled first, we automatically pick up a garment and thrust in our left or right hand first as habit dictates. So it is with fastening the buttons, which we *always* fix in a certain way. This reliance on repeated routine improves our performance, speeds our responses and reduces our need for constant decision-making.

These carefully acquired habits govern a large part of our waking lives. By the age of twenty-five we are all, according to psychologist William James, a 'bundle of habits'. If these habits are bad our health will be poor. If the habits are appropriately chosen, our physical and mental health will be sound.

We often excuse our misdemeanours on the grounds that we are *creatures* of habit. This is undoubtedly true, but the defence is poor, since it overlooks the fact that we are also *creators* of habit. If we want to achieve optimum health and happiness, we do not need to become introspective health fanatics or neurotic fitness freaks. All we need to do is establish a healthy routine of action

75

and thought. Then our bodies will take automatic care of themselves, without our constant concern and intervention.

The creation of this hygienic routine should be a major preoccupation of parents and teachers. Children should be taught the habits of health, just as they are now taught to read and write. This view was more widely accepted in the past than it is today, when the emphasis has been switched to giving children the freedom to lead their own lives and to choose their own patterns of behaviour. Whether this policy of educational *laissez-faire* has worked is open to question, particularly in view of the rise in juvenile crime, the high incidence of sexually transmitted disease and illegitimate pregnancies among teenagers, the tragic toll of adolescent suicide and mental breakdown, and the frequent newspaper reports of youngsters hooked on gambling, drugs and credit card abuse. In the face of these grim statistics one questions whether young children are always wise enough, or mature enough, to make choices which may mar their lives or hasten their deaths. As adults we accept the responsibility of teaching our children not to touch burning coals, and not to eat poisonous berries. Should we not be equally ready to teach them not to play with fire by touching drugs of addiction, and not to damage their emotional health by swallowing poisonous thoughts? This is a responsibility which most adults shirk, according to the headmaster of a British public school who reports: 'Modern parents are generally frightened not merely of teaching moral lessons, but also of taking any action to enforce them.'

This was not so in Plato's day, when the whole purpose of education was to inculcate habits of healthy behaviour. 'I mean by education,' Plato wrote in his *Laws*, 'that training which is given by suitable habits to the first instincts of virtue in children.' These traits were instilled in a number of ingenious ways. One involved the playing of a game with counters which all bore the name of one of the virtues. This process of education by habit training was further developed in seventeenth-century England, as John Locke, the philosopher/physician, describes in *Some Thoughts Concerning Education*. 'The great thing to be minded in education is what habits you settle; and therefore in this, as all other things, do not begin to make anything customary, the practice whereof you would not have continue and increase.' This is a principle of great importance and universal application.

Like Plato, Locke stressed the need to begin this habit training at the earliest possible age. This sage advice is supported by the findings of recent studies carried out by a team of Harvard psychologists led by Dr Burton White. These researchers have investigated the behaviour of infants in their first few years of life, to discover the factors which encourage the development of human competence. They found that some toddlers were far better than others at coping with the problems of everyday life, a skill which was clearly set during the first twelve months of their lives, largely as a result of the youngsters' interaction with their mothers. We learn better by emulation than by exhortation. This too was appreciated by Locke, who wrote, 'Of all the ways whereby children are to be instructed, and their manners formed, the plainest, easiest and most efficacious is to set before their eyes the examples of those things you would have them do, or avoid.'

Statistics show that schoolchildren are twice as likely to smoke if their parents smoke. So if we want our offspring to avoid the dangers of smoking-related diseases, we should set them an example of non-smoking. This is a far more effective deterrent than bribery or exhortation. In the same way, if we want them to be charitable, we should provide them with regular examples of philanthropic behaviour. This was demonstrated by an experiment conducted by Dr David Rosenhan of Swathmore College, Pennsylvania, which showed how easy it is to teach children altruistic behaviour by example alone. In the experiment a group of children took turns in playing a table-top bowling game with the experimenter. The winners of each encounter were rewarded with two gift certificates, which could be exchanged for goods at a local store. When playing with some of the children the experimenter pocketed his winning tokens. With the others he made a point of slipping one of the certificates into a box marked 'Orphans' Fund' – without comment or emphasis. Later the children were left to play the game on their own, while the researchers watched them through a one-way observation mirror.

During this period they found that nearly half the children who had been exposed to the philanthropic example chose to contribute a large proportion of their prize certificates to the Orphans' Fund, unlike the others who never made this charitable gesture. As Dr Rosenhan commented, 'Altruistic models, even in a narrow laboratory situation, serve to facilitate altruism in children.'

If we want our children to be brave, we must set them an example of brave behaviour. In the same way if we want them to be kind, or tidy, or loving, or witty, or prudent we must take care to provide them with regular examples of the behaviour we wish them to emulate. The child is the father of the man, and the parent the model for the child. We learn our virtues and social skills in our parents' arms. This is equally true of other primate species, as Japanese anthropologist Syunzo Kawamura discovered when he carried out a study of troops of monkeys. Leadership authority is handed down in dynasties, he found, because it depends on the possession of certain social skills which can only be acquired through observation. As a result simian patriarchies are formed, in which alpha animals pass on their qualities of leadership and dominance to their offspring, who in their turn become accepted as the natural leaders of the pack.

At one time children were named after the virtues – Grace, Prudence, Charity and Constance – in the hope that they would aspire to the qualities by which they were known and constantly called. At bedtime they were told moral tales of philanthropy, courage, kindness and courtesy, which aided the moulding of their characters. When they grew old enough to read for themselves, their parents chose their literature with care. In Victorian times the popular books for teenagers were not whodunits and science fiction, but moral tomes like *Noble Words and Noble Deeds*, Lord Avebury's *The Use of Life* or Samuel Smiles' *Self-Help, Character and Thrift*. These books provided children with moral guidance and encouragement.

Nowadays ethical training is no longer considered the foundation stone of education. Parents may smother their children with material gifts – personal radios, computer games and mountain bicycles – yet starve them of affection and care and moral tuition. Societies in the past invariably appointed teachers of wisdom and morality, who held an exalted place within the community. The Greeks had their sages, the Hindus their gurus, the Jews their priests, the sufis their *murshid* and the Buddhists their *bhikkus*. These enlightened individuals were specialists in character training. Now we have experts offering training in every conceivable art and craft from macramé and millinery to *maquillage* and the martial arts – but no secular teachers of ethics and moral behaviour.

Education today is gaining an increasingly vocational bias. We train children to become lawyers, doctors and engineers, but not to become healthy, happy, law-abiding citizens. We teach them to make a good living but not to make a good life. We spend our resources providing them with instruction in physics and computer science, but cannot find time to teach them ethical standards. This, say the vast majority of educationalists, is a luxury we cannot afford to support. Yet this is the one topic which we, as civilised nations, cannot afford to ignore. Mr Douglas Hurd, when British Home Secretary, drew attention to this appalling neglect when speaking recently at a meeting organised by the English Speaking Union at Oxford University. Almost half of the crimes in Britain – muggings, rapes, robberies and acts of violence and vandalism – are now committed by youngsters under the age of twenty-one. Obviously we are not teaching our young 'the unspoken social contract which binds us all in mutual care and concern'. The remedy? Douglas Hurd believes that while parents bear the prime responsibility for passing on moral standards, this is a duty which schools can no longer shirk. And so he called on teachers to debate how training in 'personal responsibility, self-discipline and civil duty' could best be reintroduced within the school curriculum.

Past experience suggests that there are four main ways in which we can teach ethical standards and life skills. These constitute the Four Es of behavioural education – example, exhortation, expectation and emulation. Of these four techniques, teaching by example is likely to prove the most effective, as Locke surmised and contemporary laboratory research has proved. Exhortation – the do's and don'ts approach – is much less productive, since it often triggers off the 'Wet Paint' response, when we are tempted to show our independence by acting directly contrary to the instructions we receive. Children 'accidentally' drop their box of toys when they are urged to be quiet and adults go out of their way to touch the wet paint they are specifically asked to avoid. If it is to produce behavioural change, exhortation normally needs to be reinforced by personal example.

Expectation is a more devious way of coaxing desired patterns of behaviour, which works by creating self-fulfilling prophesies. If we credit children with the attribute of being exceptionally tidy or polite, they feel inclined to act in such a way that they earn these particular plaudits. In the same way if we praise our neighbours in advance for their kindness, they feel obliged to live up to this reputation by carrying home our supermarket shopping or mowing our lawns when we are away on holiday. The effectiveness of this ruse has been demonstrated by experiments carried out by psychologists R. Rosenthal and L. Jacobson, and described in their book *Pygmalion in the Classroom*. They took certain first-year schoolchildren at random and provided them with fake test reports. These phoney assessments gave an inflated picture of their abilities, and suggested both to the pupils themselves and their teachers that they were destined for great things. Even though this promise had no basis in fact, the youngsters did in fact out-perform their peers in the year which followed, showing that we do indeed live up to people's expectations.

The early Greek educators probably used this technique to model the behaviour of their pupils, even though they placed far greater emphasis on the fourth stratagem of moral education – emulation. Every culture has had its heroes. Medieval Christians were encouraged to model their lives on those of the saints, who were their chosen paragons of piety and devotion. The warrior tribes of pagan Europe reared their children on tales of derring-do and valour performed by fabled Saxon lords and Viking chiefs. *Beowulf*, the earliest written poem in the English language, is devoted to such an exemplary legend. It recounts the story of a man who, with great bravery and self-sacrifice, rescued the

Danish king Hrothgar from the captive arms of Grendel, the Water Demon. In all these panegyrics, society has chosen heroes who typify the qualities it wants to promote. Victorian England had a need for explorers and colonisers, so it idolised men like Drake, Rhodes, Scott, Livingstone and Captain Cook. When the American colonialists wanted to foster the honesty of their children, they held before them the sterling example of the young George Washington, who confessed that he was the culpable tree feller, saying: 'Father, I cannot lie.' In the same manner when the Dutch wanted to encourage public-spirited behaviour, they published hagiographs about Little Hans, the boy who had saved his community from flooding by using his finger to plug a hole in a leaking dyke.

In promoting these heroes, society has recognised that it is far easier to follow a person than to pursue a philosophy or creed. If Christianity had been an impersonal collection of ethical principles it would never have spread so rapidly, nor would it have captured the hearts of simple people who could emulate the life of a cherished individual, even when they could not read a holy text or follow a theological argument. In this respect it is interesting to note that when St Paul stated the foundation of his core beliefs in his second letter to Peter, he did not say 'I know *what* I have believed', but 'I know *whom* I have believed.' So the Greeks offered their youngsters a wide selection of heroes and gods – Apollo, Theseus, Jason, Achilles, Hercules, Orestes and Agamemnon. Their tales were captured in numerous epic poems, which the Greek children were given to read in school. The purpose of this instruction was clearly stated by Socrates in *Protagorus*, one of the earliest educational texts. 'In these are contained many admonitions, and many tales and praises, and encomia of ancient famous men, which he is required to learn by heart, in order that he may imitate or emulate them and desire to become like them.'

Generally we do not elevate people to the status of public hero until they are dead. This avoids the risk that they might be toppled from their lofty pedestals by scandalous revelations about their private lives. Invariably we eulogise our heroes, glossing over their weaknesses and human failings. This we do for convenience, rather than from conscious deceit. It is not that we set out to idealise the individual; but that we have a deep-felt need to personalise the ideal. It does not matter that some of our heroes never existed; nor that in many cases they did not utter the memorable words with which they are credited, nor performed their legendary deeds of valour. If they did not exist in fact we have had to create them in fiction – because they served the vital function of acting as models of behavioural training.

Today we no longer idolise these cultural paragons. We live in the age of the anti-hero, in which it is fashionable to bestow praise on anarchic students and maverick pop stars. Sadly, when we do so, we choose to focus on their vices rather than their virtues – making a feature of their drug-taking, their drunkenness, their boorish manners and their contempt for generally accepted social values. As a result we are encouraging imitation of their brutishness, rather than emulation of their devotion to a cause, their capacity for hard work or their ability to compose some excellent music.

Previous generations were brought up with firm moral principles which were guidelines as invaluable to them as an early navigator's sextant and compass. 'Love your neighbour', was the motto on many living-room walls. 'A soft answer turneth away wrath', was the theme of countless sermons. 'Do unto others as you would have them do to you', was the Golden Rule taught in schools. Now we take our moral lead from the TV screen rather than the pulpit, and so we follow the casual example of the stars of the TV soap opera, rather than the exemplary behaviour of the wise men, priests and prophets of holy writ. In our working lives we have abandoned the principles of 'A fair day's work for a fair day's wage'; and 'A gentleman's word is his bond'. In their place we have substituted the battle cries of the business jungle, where the watchwords are 'Dog eats dog', 'God helps those who help themselves', and 'Blow you Jack I'm all right'. In the process we may make more money, and amass more material goods, but while doing so we may sacrifice our serenity, health and peace of mind.

We live in a democracy, and perhaps we recoil from the idea of creating a corps of behaviourally superior individuals, even if this élite group is composed of mythical and long-dead heroes. But we, as much as the ancient Greeks and pagan Saxon tribes, need our ethical mentors and spiritual guides.

If we are to optimise our physical well-being, and maximise our happiness, we must use all the age-old techniques of moral education – example, exhortation, expectation and emulation – to establish the habits of behavioural health. And this we must do consistently and continually.

We create ourselves – our prevailing moods, our happiness and health – by exercising our freedom of choice. Many of us start to exercise this control only when we fall sick. This is like trying to learn to swim when the ship is sinking. The time to adopt a sound philosophy of health is *now*, when we still have the rest of life ahead of us. Besides, it is a mistake to think of sickness and health as polarised extremes. Nobody is as sick as they might be, nor as healthy as they could be. Health is a continuum, a straight line on which we can journey either to the left or to the right. Wherever we stand on the line today we know that the position can be changed tomorrow. So we should not be complacent about our current level of health, nor despondent about our present state of sickness. Wherever we stand on the continuum of health the quality of our lives can be improved by adopting the principles of psychosanity outlined in the second section of this book. And the more firmly and frequently we repeat these habits of life-enhancing behaviour, the more powerful and deeply engrained they will become. Habit is said to be second nature, but this is an understatement according to the Duke of Wellington. 'Habit,' he stressed, 'is ten times nature.' To illustrate this point he told the story of a well-disciplined veteran soldier who became the victim of a practical joke soon after he returned to civilian life. The man was carrying his lunch on a tray when he heard a voice nearby shout 'Attention!'. Immediately he jumped to attention, his arms rigidly by his side, his food cascading on the floor. Such is the force of habit.

In recent years doctors have emphasised the need for life-style engineering. They have recognised that while they can offer palliative treatment for many chronic disease processes – heart disease, high blood pressure, peptic ulcers and cancer – they cannot offer cure. As a result attention is being switched from expensive high-tech treatment to low-cost, preventive education. We are being encouraged to adopt a new physical life-style, which incorporates more exercise, less drinking and smoking and a healthier pattern of eating. But this new policy – of health by habit change – has stopped far short of achieving its full potential, for it has ignored the truth expounded in this book: **that the single most important factor in the promotion of health and the prevention of disease is a healthy mental attitude.** The acceptance of this fact, and the promotion of a range of psychoprophylactic attitudes, will usher in a new era of health care.

In the past there has been no shortage of ethical creeds, the earliest of which were the Ten Commandments, given to Moses on Mount Sinai. This moral code was amplified by Jesus Christ in his Sermon on the Mount. St Paul offered a slightly different list of virtues in his second letter to Peter – love, joy, peace, patience, kindness, goodness, faithfulness, gentleness and self-control. If we think these traits are desirable we can, by constant repetition, make them as much an habitual part of our daily lives as brushing our teeth or combing our hair. This was the policy adopted by Benjamin Franklin, who identified thirteen separate attributes that he wanted to acquire – temperance, silence, order, resolution, frugality, industry, sincerity, justice, moderation, cleanliness, tranquillity, chastity and humility. During the day he would set aside periods of solitude when he could focus his attention on these qualities, one at a time. 'My intention being to acquire the habitude of all these,' he wrote, 'I judged it would be well not to distract my attention by attempting the whole at once, but to fix it on one at a time, then to proceed to another, and so on, till I should have gone through the thirteen.'

Nowadays it is no longer fashionable to preach virtue or to practise a philosophy of healthy-mindedness. This was revealed by a recent survey, conducted by *Christianity Today*, which showed that while 84 per cent of Americans still believe in the validity of the Ten Commandments, more than half could not identify even *half* of them.

It is becoming increasingly clear that if in the future we are to achieve a Utopian state – a perfect blend of contentment, physical fitness and social harmony – we need to dispense not drugs, but life-enhancing mental attitudes. As we approach the twenty-first century we will still need to follow the laws of physical hygiene, which have been so carefully delineated in recent years, but to these we must add the laws of mental hygiene, which have yet to be defined. The passport to Huxley's Brave New World will be offered not by drugs but by life-enhancing mental attitudes.

Much research remains to be done to identify these life-enhancing mental traits, and to assess their relative contribution to the wheal of human health and happiness. But enough is known to write this book, which represents the first attempt to define and categorise the states of mind which are conducive to health and which play a major role in combating disease. Some emotional attitudes – such as fear, bitterness, anger, resentment – have a *malignant* effect on the body. Others promote happiness, well-being and increased resistance to disease. For this reason, they might very well be called the *benignant* attitudes, or b-Attitudes, the term which will be used to the end of this book. Each chapter which follows is devoted to one of the seven b-Attitudes of Health. This early, tentative formulation will undoubtedly be subjected to continuing modification as more is discovered about the role of mental attitudes in the maintenance of health and the prevention of disease.

One thing is certain, that the acquisition of these beneficial attitudes will have widespread effects since they act synergistically. In this they are unlike the precepts of physical health which have a purely circumscribed effect. Eating bran, for instance, improves the function of the bowels but does nothing to improve interpersonal relationships. In the same way, jogging increases the efficiency of the heart and lungs but does little to increase happiness. (Have you ever seen a happy jogger?) Following the seven b-Attitudes of Health, on the other hand, will bring not only health but also friendship, joy and peace of mind. If this is not so they are being incorrectly practised. As Robert Louis Stevenson said in a somewhat similar context: 'If your morals make you dreary, depend upon it they are wrong.'

The widespread observance of the b-Attitudes of Health will improve the well-being of individuals, helping to turn an 'I' generation into an 'us' generation.

In identifying these characteristics I have depended partly on personal experience gained during over thirty years of medical practice, and partly on the findings of recent medical research. My indebtedness to these research workers is vast, and since their contributions are too numerous to be singled out for individual praise, I wish here to pay tribute to them all, and express to each one of them my gratitude and thanks. Without them, this book could not have been written.

I have also drawn heavily on the work of numerous philosophers and religious teachers. To them I am deeply indebted, and in regard to their contribution I can only echo Montaigne's words: 'It could be said of me that in this book I have only made up a bunch of other men's flowers, providing of my own only the string that ties them together.'

Endless books have been published giving practical advice on *physical* fitness – how to slim, eat sensibly, stop smoking, maintain a good posture, develop shapelier legs, stay young or overcome tiredness. This book fills the urgent need for a practical guide to healthy *thinking*. The chapters which follow fulfil two basic purposes:

1. They identify the attitudes of mind which can prevent disease and promote health and happiness.

2. They provide practical guidance on how these life-enhancing mental attitudes can be acquired.

So now to a description of the seven b-Attitudes of Health which, by a process of constant reiteration, must be made an habitual part of our daily lives. In this way we can become the creators of our destiny rather than the hapless victims of the hand of fate. This process of self-creation is aptly described by the anonymous writer who observed: 'Sow and act and you reap a habit; sow a habit and you reap a character; sow a character and you reap a destiny.'

# Part II

# Chapter Eight:

# COMMITMENT
## The First b-Attitude of Health

Early in my career I noticed something special about patients who appeared to be outstandingly healthy, vibrant, successful and contented – they were all highly motivated to attain clearly defined, self-appointed goals. None were aimlessly drifting through life. All were committed to a cause – which might be tracing their family tree, growing prize dahlias, building a family business or furthering the Marxist cause. This was their *raison d'être*, the existential core which gave their lives purpose, hope and drive.

This is so constant a feature of people who have mastered the art of successful living that it merits selection as the first of the seven b-Attitudes of Health.

When our forebears listed sloth as the seventh deadly sin, it was because they believed that idleness predisposed to wickedness. Satan, they were repeatedly told, would always find work for idle hands to do. Whatever the truth of this assertion, there is ample proof that idleness is a major predisposing cause of sickness. This was the basic theme of *Fit for Life*, an earlier book of mine in which I demonstrated the links between idleness and many of today's most prolific diseases, such as chronic fatigue, anxiety, depression, rheumatic pain, obesity, coronary disease and premature ageing. So obvious is this association, that these ailments are often referred to as the Hypokinetic Diseases – the diseases caused by lack of activity.

The human animal, like all other mammals, is equipped for a life of high activity. When the natural movements of captive animals are restricted, they automatically indulge in frivolous substitution gestures. Some stamp their feet, others bob or shake their heads. A captive mongoose will 'shake to death' a piece of inert meat. A caged feral cat will toy with a dead rat, tossing it into the air so that it will have an excuse to pounce on it when it falls. In this way they attempt to replace the purposeful activity of their normal lives.

Modern man, trapped in his concrete cage, has been far less successful at introducing these compensatory activities. Evolution has prepared us to cope with the excitements and hazards of life in the primeval forest, not to withstand the routine passivity of our contemporary urban life. Technology provides us today with labour-saving gadgetry with which we can brush our teeth, grind our coffee, polish our shoes, carve our meat and open our cans of baked beans. Autocratic governments shield us from responsibility by providing us with care from the cradle to the grave. In this way we have become sleeping partners in the business of life rather than executive directors.

As a result many people are experiencing feelings of boredom, futility and purposelessness. This mood of self-destruction has been a prominent feature of twentieth-century life, as Jung reported in *Modern Man in Search of a Soul*, in which he said: 'About a third of my cases are suffering from no clearly definable neurosis, but from the senselessness and emptiness of their lives. This can be described as the general neurosis of our time.'

A number of people attempt to overcome this emptiness by indulging in frivolous pastimes – parties, gambling, drug-taking, drinking sprees and casual sexual affairs – activities which, as their name suggests, pass time but do nothing to satisfy our deep-seated need for purposeful employment. This was the escape route taken by Ecclesiastes, the wise and wealthy Jew, who spent the early part of his life seeking happiness by amassing wealth, acquiring power and enjoying sexual conquests. But none of these quests satisfied his underlying yearning. Whatever he undertook it gave him little lasting pleasure, since he knew it was doomed to end in death. 'All is vanity', was his pessimistic deduction at the end of his long, sybaritic search. Then, as he grew older, he found a way of filling his life with meaning. The secret lay in the way he occupied each passing moment. If he squandered his time because each fleeting hour took him one step nearer to the grave, life seemed grim and futile. But if he filled each passing moment with significance and purpose, life immediately acquired meaning, worth and satisfaction.

Many people today are like the young Ecclesiastes. They fritter away the present because they know it cannot last, when they should be filling it with purpose for the very reason that it *is* ephemeral. Our portion in life, Ecclesiastes discovered, is the sum of all our daily labours. The more we give, the more we gain. So we should live each day with fervour and full commitment, even if we are doing no more than cleaning the car or baking a cake. In the words of Ecclesiastes: 'Whatever thy hand findest to do, do it with all thy might.' That is the way to overcome the sense of purposelessness which remains, as it was in Jung's day, one of the great sicknesses of our age.

There is evidence that a sense of purpose and commitment provides us with a reason to live and a powerful motivation to stay alive, even when the dice are loaded against us. This was the driving force which kept Lauren Elder alive when the privately chartered Cessna plane in which she was flying crashed into the ice-capped peaks of the High Sierra mountains. The crash killed her two companions, and left Lauren with a fractured arm and badly strained leg. Somehow she survived the shock, the intense cold and the repeated hallucinations. Despite her weakened condition, she struggled unshod over the rugged terrain until her feet were almost bare of flesh. What kept her going? Simply the desire to live and the will to complete the work she had set out to perform. 'I had so much left to do,' she explained afterwards, 'There were so many places I had not been, so many people I had not met, so much work to be done. I had not laughed enough, or learned enough or felt enough. I had not borne a child.' It was her strong commitment to these causes which enabled her to summon up the strength of mind and body to overcome her terrifying ordeal.

A firm sense of purpose can preserve our lives, as sociologist David Phillips discovered when he carried out a study of Jews living in New York and Budapest, and found that the anticipation of a meaningful event improved their expectation of life. He discovered a notable drop in their death rate before Yom Kippur, the Day of Atonement, for instance, a fall which was not observed in their non-Jewish neighbours. He also found that they were less likely to die in the days of gently mounting excitement leading up to their birthdays, a drop which was balanced by a correspondingly increased mortality rate when their anniversary celebrations were over. 'Some people,' Phillips concluded, 'look forward to witnessing certain important occasions and are able to put off dying in order to do so.'

For some individuals it is the appeal of work, rather than the attraction of birthdays or religious festivals, which provides the necessary driving force. A statue in the grounds of Canterbury Cathedral provides permanent evidence of this fact. It is the crowning achievement in the career of David McFall, the Scottish sculptor who developed inoperable cancer in his early sixties which left him so enfeebled that he was forced to abandon his work. Then he received a commission to create a seven-foot statue of Christ for the gardens of Britain's premier cathedral. His doctors told him that it was 'fanciful in the extreme' to imagine that he could complete the work, which involved clambering over scaffolding and performing hard manual labour which would have taxed even a young, fit man. But McFall was enthused and felt he had to try. 'At this the evening of my life,' he told his friends, 'I regard it as a miracle from heaven.' So he struggled through the pain and overwhelming lassitude, his badly disfigured face hidden behind a Phantom of the Opera mask. He determined that *nothing*, not even his medical treatment, should interfere with his work. In keeping with that resolve he refused an operation to remove three ribs, knowing that it would impair the strength of his upper body. So he laboured on, even when his body grew emaciated by the loss of several stone in weight. His doctors expected him to collapse at any moment, and yet he dragged himself on, even when he was so exhausted at the end of his working day that it took him one and a half hours to replace the protective wrappings around his monumental figure. Eventually the work was completed, cast and painstakingly hand-finished. Only when the sculpture was packed and ready for despatch to Canterbury Cathedral did David McFall cease to drive his weary frame. Then he died, his work completed. The specialist who cared for him throughout his long ordeal told reporters that his absorption in his work had given him the strength to surmount his weakness and pain. 'It was the Christ sculpture,' he said, 'that gave him the will to live.'

As indicated earlier, gerontologists have confirmed that hard work, providing it is satisfying, is not a killer but an elixir of life.

Not everyone, however, is engaged in congenial work. Many have jobs which are meaningless, dull and repetitive. For them the return to work after a refreshing weekend break, is always a time of crisis. This explains the Black Monday Syndrome, a phenomenon well known to statisticians. An analysis of nearly 2,000 American suicides, conducted by the Harvard School of Public Health, underlined the reality of the Monday 'blues', for it showed that people are more likely to kill themselves on a Monday than on any other day of the week. A similar review of coronary deaths in Britain, carried out by the Office of Population Censuses and Surveys, revealed that Monday is a danger time for heart attacks in men of working age. The fact that this trend is less marked in men over the age of sixty suggests that the crisis is work related. This link is further confirmed by the researcher's observation that the peak death rate from heart attacks shifts to a Tuesday when the week begins with a leisurely Bank Holiday!

Work is an unmitigated blessing only when it is satisfying and congenial. But despite this caveat, the vast majority of people are healthier when they are occupied than when they are idle. Most people would anticipate a relationship between depression and unemployment, but how many could accurately estimate the strength of this association? The closeness of the link was revealed by a three-year study in the city of Oxford, which showed that attempted suicide was *twelve* to *fifteen* times more common among unemployed men than in those of similar age who had a permanent job. Lack of daily employment also predisposes to heart disease according to a British survey, which provides a partial explanation for the 21 per cent higher death rates recorded by unemployed British men.

Lack of full-time work also makes people more prone to visit their doctors with complaints of coughs and colds. This may be because they have time to kill, or because their immunity to infection is lowered by the stress of unemployment. This latter possibility is supported by the discovery of research workers at the Bethesda Hospital in America, who took blood tests and found that unemployed men and women suffer a drop in their white blood cell count and an increase in their circulatory levels of cortisol, the stress hormone which among other functions suppresses the efficiency of the immune system. Subsequent blood analyses showed that both of these biological changes – which temporarily impair the body's ability to cope with infection – were reversed when the subjects resumed full-time employment.

Retirement, like unemployment, is another crisis time for many individuals. Our forebears worked until they chose to retire, or until they were no longer capable of performing their chosen occupations. Then came the dreadful imposition of a compulsory retirement age towards the end of the nineteenth century. This forced people to cease work whether they wished to or not and, far more significantly, whether they had purposeful work to retire to, or were being sentenced to spend the remainder of their days in aimless idleness. This ill-judged piece of legislation has been the sickening of many lives, and the shortening of countless others, for as a spokesman fopr the Soviet Institute of Gerontology has said: 'Man could live longer if he were allowed to work longer.' This view is supported by research conducted at the Johns Hopkins Memorial Hospital in conjunction with a number of leading American life insurance companies, which revealed that 'the right occupation' comes high on the list of factors leading to a long, productive life.

Many people are concerned that increasing age will make them incapable of work, but the facts do not support this commonly held fear. When doctors from Birmingham University carried out a survey of a thousand men aged between sixty-five and seventy they found that nine out of ten were fit to carry on with their jobs. Bringing work to an abrupt halt at this, or at any other artificial 'retirement' age can cause a decline in health by removing life's prime *raison d'être*. Sometimes it is a straightforward question of do or die. This was the warning issued by Jeremy Taylor, the seventeenth-century prelate. 'Idleness,' he pronounced, 'is the death of a living man.' (In the past the traditional allocation of sex roles favoured women, since they were not forcibly retired, which may explain why female centenarians outnumber males by six to one.)

An enjoyable occupation appears to be one of the secrets of perennial youth. Pablo Casals, the world famous cellist, published his biography when he was ninety-three. In it he wrote: 'Work helps to prevent one getting old. I for one cannot dream of retiring . . . My work is my life. I cannot think of one without the other. The man who works and is never bored is never old.'

A few years ago a Swiss pharmaceutical company made a survey of elderly workers in Britain and found that they had over 500 claimants for the title of Britain's oldest worker. 'We have been amazed,' the firm reported, 'at the number of men in their nineties still doing a full day's work.' Even more remarkable was the old stagers' positive mental attitude towards their work. 'Working stops you feeling miserable,' said a ninety-one year old from Ramsgate in Kent who was still putting in a forty-hour week as a cleaner and decorator. 'I think work is the secret of happiness.' This view was shared by a ninety-two-year-old widower from Mitcham in Surrey who was still running a family business making window blinds. 'I love my work,' he said. 'Men die when they stop working.'

People who share Casals' commitment are generally too busy to notice the passage of time and too preoccupied to feel miserable. A doctor once asked a middle-aged lady the secret of her vitality and never-failing cheerfulness. She had brought up nine children on a farm, had done all her own housework and found time to help with the never-ending farm chores. Yet she had never had a day's illness, nor did she seem to suffer nervous exhaustion or psychosomatic aches and pains. 'How is it you managed never to have a nervous breakdown?' he asked in genuine wonder. 'You know, doctor,' she confessed, 'I've always *wanted* to have a nervous breakdown. But every time I was about to have one, it was time to get somebody a meal.'

Most people find that the easiest way to overcome spells of depression is to indulge in some form of purposeful activity. Psychological interviews with American soldiers returning from prisoner of war camps in North Vietnam revealed that most had suffered from periods of apathy and depression at some time during their internment. Closer questioning disclosed that the most successful ways of overcoming these debilitating moods was through physical exercise, establishing communication with fellow prisoners, watching insects, inventing things, playing games, maintaining health and hygiene or matching wits with the Vietcong guards. These meaningful activities bring about an elevation of mood, probably because they alter the output of neurohormones such as noradrenaline and monoamine oxidase (both of which play an important part in the metabolism of the brain).

In addition to being a source of happiness, work is also the pathway to personal fulfilment as demonstrated by Abraham Maslow's lifetime study of people who appeared to have most nearly succeeded in achieving their full intellectual, emotional and physical potential. 'In all cases, at least in our culture,' he concluded, 'they are dedicated people devoted to some task "outside themselves", some vocation or duty or beloved job.' We achieve fulfilment, and give purpose to our lives, through our personal commitments. If we choose we can devote our lives to building a magnificent garden, healing the sick, teaching children, writing plays, bringing up a family, making a fortune, inventing toys, or creating works of art. Much of our identity is tied up in these activities. In medieval times men were named after their occupations as Smith, Turner, Mason, Carpenter or Cartwright. (Or in the case of immigrant Jewish tailors and goldsmiths as Schneider and Goldschmidt.) Even today in the outlying parts of Wales men are known as 'Jones the Milk' or

'Davies the Post'. Man is identified less by his rank and wealth than by his work. Few people today would know the names of the rich citizens of ancient Athens, but most could recall the names of her illustrious poets and philosophers. In the same way thousands revere the work of the great Johann Sebastian Bach, but how many can recall, or ever knew, the name of the wealthy prince who gave him patronage? Man's work is his greatest monument.

One of the great temptations for *homo sapiens* is to dream rather than act. But dreams cannot clean a pair of shoes, nor can meditation mend a broken fuse or psychological introspection cook a meal. When a power cut occurs it is better to light a candle than to sit back and wait for the restoration of the power supply. This was the advice of Carlyle who said: 'The end of man is an action and not a thought, though it were the noblest.' Even the ancient mystics recognised this, for Ignatius, St Theresa and the ancient Zen masters agreed that the whole purpose of the contemplative life was to fit a person for action.

Through our work we gain success, status, fulfilment and self-esteem. Nothing worthwhile is achieved without toil. All the great monuments to man's creative endeavour – the pyramids, the Panama canal, the Taj Mahal – were constructed as a result of hours of unremitting, corporate effort. The construction of Stonehenge is estimated to have taken more than 18 million man-hours of labour, a colossal enterprise which must have engaged a large proportion of the British population for years on end. Never again are we likely to see such a mammoth testament to man's collective zeal, for we now live in a culture which prizes competition rather than co-operation and fosters inter-group rivalry rather than teamwork. And yet even in this 'dog eats dog' milieu, there is evidence that success is still derived from grafting rather than from cut-throat competition. This was confirmed when psychologists studied the career patterns of a group of scientists and a number of graduates from the University of Texas School of Business Studies. Contrary to popular opinion and expectation, the researchers found that the survey's most successful individuals recorded lower than average scores for competitiveness. Where they scored highly was on their keen desire to work hard and to tackle challenging tasks. This was the attribute which singled them out from their less successful colleagues and drove them to the top. Among the scientists it was noted that 'a high degree of competitiveness tended to have deleterious effects on the production of influential work among otherwise motivated scientists'. With the business graduates it was found that 'the highest income was received by those high in work-mastery and low in competitiveness'.

The elevated risk of coronary disease among Type A subjects is unlikely to be caused by their devotion to work, as was originally thought, but is probably closely linked to their aggression and ruthless competitiveness. These largely negative emotions have previously been promoted as essential weapons in the battle for personal success, but must now be recognised as potent tools of self-destruction.

The Victorians made a religion of the work ethic. One of their most respected spokesmen, Thomas Carlyle, regarded it as one of the greatest of all beatitudes. 'Blessed is the man who has found his work,' he wrote. 'Let him ask no other blessedness.' This may seem to be making a virtue of what was nothing more than a grim, economic necessity to many living in the nineteenth-century industrial slums. Yet there is no doubt that work which is personally fulfilling *does* bestow a wide variety of blessings. It promotes health, dispels boredom, creates wealth, gives purpose to life, provides an outlet for creativity, self-expression and skill, enhances self-esteem and affords regular opportunities for social contact. In some cases it even secures a measure of immortality.

The Talmud suggests that there are three things we should do before we die – have a child, plant a tree and write a book. It is no coincidence that all three of these achievements leave monuments to our existence which survive our death. To this extent the people who create a glorious garden, found a family dynasty, write an opera or discover a life-saving drug earn for themselves a degree of lasting recognition. Their bodies die, but their work lives on. St Paul's Cathedral contains a memorial tablet to its creator Sir Christopher Wren which does not attempt to catalogue his brilliant architectural achievements, but says quite simply: 'If you seek his monument look around you.' A similar tablet is attached to the walls of Liverpool Cathedral: 'Here lies in honour all that could die of a pioneer in orthopaedics, Sir Robert Jones.' Graves imprison bodies, but cannot inter achievements. This fundamental truth was recognised by Horace, the Roman poet, who wrote: '*Non omnis moriar*' (I shall not all die).

Many of the social benefits bestowed by history's great heroes, benefactors and philanthropists have been instigated in an attempt to secure for themselves a permanent place in the hall of fame. Alfred Nobel, the Swedish chemist, made a vast fortune out of his invention of dynamite and other high explosives; but he is far better known today as the founder of five, annually bestowed Nobel Prizes. This is the way he wished, and deliberately chose, to be remembered. Few people have the chance to draft their entry in the annals of fame. Nobel's opportunity came when his brother died and a Swedish newspaper inadvertently published *his* obituary. Alfred read the notice and was shocked to discover that he was described, and would be remembered, as the man who had made a fortune out of creating explosives which had changed the dimensions of modern warfare by creating new techniques of mass annihilation. This was not the way he wished to be remembered. So, to counteract his image as a merchant of destruction, he decided to use a large part of his vast fortune to create a series of highly esteemed international awards. In this way he would be remembered with affection, not as malefactor, but as a public benefactor.

This may seem to be a contrived and mercenary way of buying prestige. And yet can there be any harm in working to achieve the esteem of one's fellows, if such work satisfies the individual and at the same time benefits society itself? Professor Hans Selye made a lifetime study of the effects of stress on human behaviour. In the course of this work he developed a simple yet profound philosophy of life, which he described as altruistic egotism. He recognised that self-interest and self-protection are basic human drives. As man's life became more sophisticated, he discovered the advantages of working in groups. Even in the primeval forest it was necessary to form bands to hunt and fight.

Generations later when man moved into the big industrial cities it became increasingly necessary to place the public interest before the immediate gratification of personal whims and wants. The resolution of this conflict between the desires of the individual and the needs of the group is the *sine qua non* of civilisation. Selye believed that this vital process of acculturation can be fostered by observing the principle of altruistic egotism. By this he meant that we, like Alfred Nobel, should order our actions in such a way that they secure the long-term benefit of the community as well as the fulfilment of our own, immediate desires.

'Love thy neighbour as thyself' is the biblical counsel of altruistic perfection. Selye modified this injunction to 'Earn thy neighbour's love'. This creates a principle which is easier to observe and more immediately rewarded, since by winning our neighbour's love we also gain their esteem and approbation. Selye, through his lifetime of writing and research, did his best to earn his neighbour's love. As he wrote: 'I am doing my utmost to give meaning to life through useful work.'

Commitment to a cause and its relationship to happiness, health and success has been demonstrated in a remarkable American study. This took a group of nearly 500 teenagers from inner-city Boston, and followed their lives and careers at regular intervals during the next forty years. The project, conducted by a team of researchers from Harvard University Medical School, was designed to throw light on the problems caused by juvenile delinquency. Many of the boys came from poor backgrounds or broken homes, conditions which are often thought to give rise to social deviance and under-achievement. Others started out with disadvantages of class, ethnic background, deficient schooling and lower-than-average IQ. Yet none of these factors appeared to determine the boys' ultimate success in life. When they were tested by independent assessors in middle age it was found that the boys' development had nothing to do with the privileges of intelligence, income or social class. What really mattered was their level of activity during their formative years. As part of their original assessment they were given an activity rating, with points awarded for their involvement in school work, sports, household chores, part-time jobs and extra-curricular activities. This proved to be the major formative influence in their lives, for the subjects who as youngsters were most fully committed to hobbies and school activities turned out to become the happiest and healthiest men, the best fathers and the most successful husbands.

This did not surprise psychiatrist Dr George Vaillant, who headed the study. 'It's not difficult to explain,' he said. 'Boys who worked in the home or community gained competence and came to feel they were worthwhile members of society. And because they felt good about themselves, others felt good about them.'

What *was* remarkable was the strength of the influence of this early childhood commitment. When they reached manhood, the boys with the highest activity ratings were twice as likely to have built up warm relationships with a wide circle of friends; five times as likely to be in well-paid jobs and sixteen times less likely to have endured significant spells of unemployment. Conversely, the less industrious youngsters were more likely to have been arrested for criminal offences and ten times more prone to have suffered mental illness. Even more significant, the mortality rates were found to be six times higher among the less-committed individuals.

Parents and educationalists must heed these findings. If we want to create a nation of fit, happy, well-adjusted individuals, we must start by teaching our children the discipline of work as well as the formal sciences of physics and mathematics. But we must do so with care, for not all work is life-enhancing. We need to encourage commitments, but not to tasks which are purposeless, unremitting, exhausting, degrading, dull or devoid of pleasure and reward. In time we will develop a hygiene of work, much as we have now devised a protocol for maintaining physical fitness. This will contain a number of guidelines to help us enjoy the multifold blessings of purposeful activity, while avoiding the equally numerous pitfalls of work obsession, job dissatisfaction and role mismatch. Even at this stage it is safe to anticipate some of the contents of this guide:

- **Work/Rest Cycles**
  *Even the most enjoyable work becomes exhausting if it is pursued too long. For this reason it is vital to intersperse periods of work with regular intervals of rest to prevent the build-up of fatigue and the onset of staleness and inefficiency. This is the biological pattern of work, observed quite naturally by animals and children, but ignored to their cost by many modern workaholics. Tests in industry show that the introduction of official rest breaks at the end of every working hour can lead to productivity increases of a tenth or more.*

- **Concentration**
  *Stress occurs, and efficiency and satisfaction decline, when we try to focus our attention on more than one task at a time. In this respect we should emulate the example of the Buddhist monks who concentrate their entire energies on the task in hand, whether it is a sacred duty like praying or a mundane chore like cleaning a pair of shoes. Too often nowadays we dissipate our energies and read a newspaper while at the same time carrying on a conversation and watching a TV programme. In the process we lose much of the value and satisfaction of all three activities. In the same way we often dissipate our energies by mulling over the past and worrying about the future when we should be enjoying the present. These deficiencies can be overcome by mastering the art of concentration on the ever present 'here and now'. This was the advice that Sir William Osler, the wise and eminent Canadian physician, gave to his worried and overworked patients. 'Throw away all ambition,' he told them, 'beyond that of doing the day's work well.'*

- **The Mental/Physical Balance**
  *Fatigue is largely task-related and never absolute. In this way there can be occasions when we are far too exhausted to fill in an income tax form, but not too tired to go fishing or play a game of bridge. This applies particularly to the tiredness caused by prolonged mental strain, which can often be eased by engaging in*

non-demanding physical work. Dr John Kellogg, the inventor of the eponymous breakfast cereals, applied this principle at his famous sanatorium at Battle Creek, Michigan, where he set nervously exhausted businessmen the simple tasks of gardening, carpentry, pottery and weaving. Similar forms of occupational therapy are used today by Shoma Morita, a leading Japanese psychiatrist. He employs the work cure to overcome neuroses, which he believes are fostered by an excess of self-preoccupation. To overcome this degree of neurotic introspection he forbids his patients to talk about their problems and sets them instead the task of working out of doors at tasks of gradually increasing intensity. This regime, he finds, increases their confidence, brings them into contact with the beauty of nature, shows them that they can work effectively despite their neuroses and helps them to lose themselves and their problems in their work.

- **External Focus**
  Psychologists and stress researchers find that people who are committed to an outside cause are generally happier, friendlier and less neurotic than those who work primarily for their own immediate benefit. This was the experience of Abraham Maslow, quoted earlier in this chapter, and also of Hans Selye who confessed: 'I never met a happy individual who was not committed to a job or cause outside himself.'

- **Personal Satisfaction**
  Work, when properly chosen, can provide an unparalleled vehicle for personal fulfilment and self-expression. But not if its sole aim is to earn money. Many people claim that they are working in soul-destroying jobs simply to earn the cash to travel or buy a luxury home and garden. But of what use is this dedication if they become so committed to their cash-creating activities that they are left with no time to travel or to potter in their gardens? Work, if it is to be beneficial, must be personally fulfilling. When a large group of English factory workers were asked to list the things which gave them job satisfaction they gave the highest rating to

103

the opportunity for advancement and learning and the chance to introduce their own ideas. Far less importance was placed on the length of working hours and the arduousness of the job. And the lure of financial reward could do no better than secure sixth place in the list of factors contributing to job satisfaction.

Many people select a job with as much care as they choose a pair of jeans. Yet on this choice their welfare and mental health depends. This was discovered by Dr William Menninger, head of the US army's neuropsychiatric division during World War Two. 'We learned much in the army as to the importance of selection and of placement, of putting the right man in the right job,' he reported. 'Where a man had no interest, where he was misplaced, where he thought he was not being appreciated, where he believed his talents were being misused, invariably we found a potential if not an actual psychiatric casualty.'

The devastating psychological effects of incongenial work were also shown by inmates in concentration camps who were often forced to perform pointless jobs like carrying cartloads of bricks backwards and forwards from place to place. Eventually frustration levels would mount until the prisoners became suicidal, sometimes ending their aimless existences by throwing themselves against the camp's electrified fences. But when the prisoners were engaged in tasks which gave them even a modicum of personal satisfaction, and the slightest chance to express their individuality, they were enabled to keep going despite the squalour, disease and inadequate nutrition. Such is the motivating force of purposeful work.

- ● **Personal Enjoyment**
  Work, as well as affording an outlet for creativity and self-expression, should also provide a source of excitement and recurrent enjoyment. One of the great tragedies of modern life is that so many people allow themselves to be indentured to jobs for which they have little enthusiasm or liking.

  A few years ago I visited Thailand to study traditional Thai medicine. I came back enriched, less from my study of oriental herbs and manipulative techniques than from my contact with the delightful Thai people who seemed outstandingly friendly, relaxed and happy. One important reason for their bonhomie is that they place greater importance on being happy than on amassing material possesions. When they are offered a new job they are naturally interested in the salary and status it offers, but more particularly they want to know if it is *sanook* which means 'fun'. We would lead healthier, happier lives if we used the same criterion when selecting jobs and spare-time activities.

Thomas Edison was one of the world's most prolific workers. He is recognised as the creator of over a thousand separate inventions, including the incandescent lamp, the phonograph and an early kinetoscopic camera. Often he would spend eighteen hours a day in his laboratory where, to save time, he would frequently eat and sleep. Yet towards the end of his life he could look back on his career and say with complete honesty: 'I never did a day's work in my life: it was all fun.'

If you cannot say the same about your current job, or your spare-time commitments, it is time for a change. You deserve better. Nobody can do justice to their work if it doesn't do justice to them, by providing them with stimulus, personal satisfaction – and *sanook*!

- Self-respect
*Over the years I have met many people whose lives have been made miserable by the shamefulness of their work. A tobacconist of my acquaintance despised himself for making a profit out of peddling what he appreciated was a carcinogenic, habit-forming drug. Several businessmen have told me that they suffer stress when they are expected to take part in shady deals which benefit the company but conflict with their own ethical standards.*

Bertrand Russell devoted an entire chapter of his book The Conquest of Happiness to the subject of work, which he regarded as potentially a major source of contentment. But he noted that many people compromise their principles and prostitute their skills in order to earn a high salary, but would be much happier with a less remunerative job which enabled them to retain their self-esteem. 'Without self-respect genuine happiness is scarcely *possible,' he wrote, 'and the man who is ashamed of his work can hardly achieve self-respect.'*

## ● Realistic Goal-setting

*However great your genius, you will never be a success if you set your sights too high. Leonardo da Vinci – artist, engineer, architect and inventor – was probably the most gifted man who ever lived. Yet he remained strangely discontented and unfulfilled, because he was never satisfied with his work. 'I wish to work miracles,' he admitted as a youth. In his maturity he could only lament his 'wasted' days. During his lifetime he had designed ratchets, winches, cranes, steam-driven pistons and differential transmissions, and made thousands of innovative drawings of technical designs and anatomical dissections; yet he constantly berated himself for not achieving more.*

*Stress arises whenever there is a gap between ambition and ability, even when the ability soars to the heights of da Vinci's genius. This experience of disappointment and self-assessed failure can cause a breakdown in health, as was revealed by the experiments carried out at West Point military academy, described earlier in this book, which showed that people who strive in vain to attain unrealistic goals have an above-average risk of developing infections such as glandular fever. The same discovery was made at Charing Cross Hospital, London, where doctors investigated the incidence of myalgic encephalomyelitis and found that the young victims of what is often called 'Yuppie Flu', had often exhausted themselves in their attempt to reach their lofty goals. 'They have four-star abilities with five-star ambitions', was the way their predicament was described by one doctor.*

*Many people suffer stress ailments – such as migraine headaches and peptic ulcers – because they are perfectionists. They set themselves goals which they cannot possibly attain, or more commonly accept without question the unrealistic standards set for them by their parents. If they are conscientious, they spend their lives in an unavailing struggle to please their parents by fulfilling their lofty aspirations. The solution to this dilemma is to establish more realistic goals and to regard success as a journey* rather than a final destination. Whatever the satisfaction of completing a difficult trek, there should also be resting points of contentment on the way. Even if we do not succeed in climbing the north face of Everest, there is pleasure to be had from scaling the lesser Himalayan foothills. We can't win every battle – but we can win some. From our successes we gain satisfaction; from our failures we acquire wisdom.

This is one of the joys of advancing age, that we become gentler with ourselves and more aware of our weaknesses and limitations. When we are twenty we want to change the world; when we are sixty we settle for changing the layout of the lounge furniture. In the words of the nineteenth-century philosopher Henry Thoreau: 'Youth gets together the materials for a bridge to the moon, and maturity uses them to build a wood-shed.' At both stages in life we should set realistic goals. Neither as teenagers nor as adults should we aim too high or attempt too little.

Others fail because they cannot accept the gifts they have. Richard Burton was a highly talented actor, but this did not give him satisfaction because he longed to be a writer. 'He would have happily rejected all his wealth and fame to have been an important author,' records his biographer Melvyn Bragg. Thomas Carlyle experienced a similar dissatisfaction. He was a brilliant writer, yet he longed to be a bridge builder like his father, and claimed that he would have preferred to have built one of his father's bridges than written all his books. This attitude also invites disappointment. Writing books is a worthy occupation; but so too is acting, farming, nursing, child-rearing and bricklaying. The secret is to make a bouquet with the flowers within your grasp.

- ## Live Life with Enthusiasm
'Zest is the secret of happiness and well-being', according to Bertrand Russell. The pauper, who tucks into his meagre bowl of porridge with relish, is more favoured than the wealthy man who derives no pleasure from his diet of wild strawberries and caviare. To be fully alive we need to be engaged in purposeful work and also to be fully committed to life itself, for as Russell observed:

*'The more things a man is interested in, the more opportunities he has for happiness.'*

*A passionate commitment to life is also the highway to success, for as Ralph Waldo Emerson remarked: 'Nothing great was ever achieved without enthusiasm.' This truth was exemplified in the life of Mark Twain, who when asked the reason for his success replied quite simply: 'I was born excited.'*

*How much would Joan of Arc, the simple maid of Orleans, have achieved had she not been fired with religious zeal? Would Christopher Columbus have found the courage and drive to pursue his hazardous voyages of discovery to America and the West Indies had he not been driven by a fervent desire to find a western passage to India and China? Everyone who has made their mark on society has been motivated by some passionate interest or desire which has enabled them to achieve their goal despite frustration, ridicule, failure, sickness, shortage of money or lack of support. As La Fontaine observed: 'Man is so made that whenever anything fires his soul, impossibilities vanish.'*

We need to live wholeheartedly, but we also need to experience an inner tranquillity and peace of mind. These qualities may sound incompatible, and yet they are found to co-exist in people with a healthy disposition, as the following chapter explains.

Chapter Nine:

# CALMNESS
## *The Second b-Attitude of Health*

Most virtues become vices when practised to excess. This is certainly true of the work ethic, which can become an unhealthy obsession if it is not kept in proportion and balanced by a calmness of disposition.

Sir Walter Scott, the great Scottish writer, took as his motto the five words: 'Never to be doing nothing.' He followed this precept so successfully that he suffered a nervous breakdown in his fifties and drove himself to an early grave by the age of sixty-one. In our achievement-oriented age many people follow Scott's example and become addicted to work as surely as others become hooked on drink or drugs. Unfortunately, while society condemns the destructive life of the alcoholic or compulsive gambler, it applauds and actively rewards the person who overworks, even when they do so to the detriment of their health.

Surveys carried out by Dr Anthony Clare at the Institute of Psychiatry, London, show that workaholics are particularly prone to suffer hypertension, peptic ulcers, migraine and coronary disease. This is not surprising since people who carry a heavy burden of unremitting work develop a variety of potentially harmful stress reactions.

The counter to this hazard, as indicated in the previous chapter, is to intersperse periods of work with regular spells of rest and relaxation. This is the work schedule given by divine ordination to the Jewish people, who were instructed to observe a sabbath day of rest at the end of each working week. The history books show that public health and safety deteriorates whenever this fundamental physiological principle is ignored. The French people were instructed to treat Sunday as a normal working day during the French Revolution, but the nation's health suffered so dramatically that the edict had to be reversed immediately the crisis ended. A similar sequence of events occurred in Britain during the Second World War when the average working week of munitions workers was increased from fifty-six to nearly seventy hours, to stave off the threat of invasion after the evacuation of Dunkirk. To begin with the factories reported a 10 per cent rise in output, but then productivity fell as sickness absenteeism mounted and accident rates soared.

Many of today's go-getting executives have been fooled into believing they must adopt a non-stop, aggressive, Type A work programme if they are to stand a chance of clawing their way to the top. In fact this is a surer recipe for a premature place in the graveyard than an early seat on the board. Dr Meyer Friedman has revealed that many American organisations and companies are headed by gentle, unhurried, relaxed, Type B individuals. He conducted a small survey which showed that 40 per cent of bank presidents were Type B personalities. So too were 45 per cent of generals, admirals, bank presidents and Nobel laureates, 50 per cent of church leaders, 57 per cent of senators and congressmen and 60 per cent of judges. So why kill yourself to get to the top, through your Type A behaviour, if you can dispense with the aggression and competitive struggle and still succeed?

Hard graft is necessary to achieve some goals, but there are other targets which are more easily attained through relaxation, gentleness and patience. This is particularly true of creative work, which often calls for an effortless use of the subconscious mind rather than great intellectual endeavour. Descartes is said to have made his most important intellectual discoveries while lazing in bed in the morning. Newton formulated the laws of gravity while lying relaxed under an apple tree. Pilkington conceived the float tank technique for making plate glass while washing up. Archimedes hit upon the laws of hydrostatics while soaking in a bath. Mozart composed one of his famous pieces of music during a game of bowls and another when he was playing billiards. Elias Howe, a Massachusetts instrument maker, got his inspiration for the automatic sewing machine in his sleep, when he dreamed that he was being chased by a native wielding a spear with a hole in it.

Invariably the creative process passes through two initial stages. First there is a period of preparation, during which the problem is studied from all conceivable angles. Then there is a period of incubation, during which the idea is allowed to develop in the subconscious mind. The first stage involves effort; the second demands time and tranquillity. Helmholtz, the famous German physicist, spoke for most inventors when he said: 'Happy ideas generally come to me unexpectedly without effort, like an inspiration. But they have never come to me when my mind was fatigued or when I was at my work table.'

This was confirmed by a survey of French scientists which revealed that 75 per cent of important technical discoveries have been made when the originators were not engaged in active research. So we should not feel guilty if we spend time in contemplation or idle revelry, for this could be the most creative part of our day, the time when we too might have a 'Eureka' experience.

Unfortunately modern society has little respect for daydreamers. We have been schooled to believe that advances can only be made by people who work long and hard. This is the view we drum into our children. 'Must try harder', we write on their end-of-term reports. But there are numerous occasions when we would achieve more by trying *less*. Effort can be self-defeating, as happens when tennis players try too hard to deliver an ace and end up serving a double fault. Through an excess of zeal a golfer misses a simple putt and an employee keen for advancement stutters at his promotion interview.

There are many occasions when it is advisable to follow the 'Softly, softly catchee monkey' approach. This attitude is favoured in the East, where people are more inclined to sit back and let things happen, than adopt the screwed-up pose favoured by the workaholic Westerner – back to the wall, nose to the grindstone and shoulder to the wheel. When the treadmill of daily life spins too rapidly only a fool pedals faster; the wise man freewheels and uses the built-up momentum to carry him on. There is no virtue in working hard if you can work easy. The goal is to achieve the maximum results with the minimum effort. Sometimes this means tempering our customary, effortful exuberance. As Lao-Tze, the great Taoist philosopher, counselled: 'Don't push the river, let it flow.'

This attitude of quiet repose becomes increasingly vital during periods of mental strain. When stress levels are excessive and prolonged we grow tense, tired and inefficient. We make an increasing number of mistakes and suffer psychosomatic symptoms – headaches, fibrositis, insomnia – which further increase our incapacity. This is the body's warning to ease up. Instead of heeding this cry we often choose to work longer and harder in a vain attempt to compensate for our inadequacies. This compounds the problem, making us more fatigued and tense and therefore still less productive. The longer this vicious cycle continues, the greater our risk of suffering a serious breakdown in health.

We always regard periods of relaxation, rest and sleep as times of complete non-productivity, whereas they are actually vital times of bodily growth. During spells of deep sleep the pituitary gland steps up its output of growth hormone and there is an associated increase in protein production. During these times of repose the bodily machinery undergoes its major servicing and repair.

All living tissues are subject to breakdown and degeneration, metabolic activities which are collectively known as catabolic processes. This differentiates them from the anabolic processes which are connected with tissue building and repair. Metabolic health is achieved when there is a balance between these two opposing trends, so that the forces of wear are matched by the forces of repair. Illness occurs whenever persistent infection, stress or overwork leads to a preponderance of the catabolic tendencies. Nowadays we may quite reasonably treat this unhealthy imbalance by giving antibiotics to cure the infection, or tranquillisers to subdue the nervous overstimulation. But a generation ago these drugs were not available. In their place doctors could only use natural recuperative methods – rest and relaxing holidays – to restore the health of a patient's metabolic balance sheet.

Two thousand years ago the Greek followers of Asclepius subjected a wide range of illnesses to a treatment known as incubation or temple sleep. A similar principle was employed in Victorian Britain to relieve the strain of life within the rapidly growing industrial cities. In 1887 a British newspaper warned its readers of the dangers of overexhaustion. 'If we cannot avoid frequent agitation,' it counselled, 'we should, if possible, give the nervous system time to recover itself between the shocks.' Later in the same article it suggested a simple way in which this could be achieved, quoting a doctor 'learned in the art of healing who pronounces a day in bed every now and then as a cure for the multiplied worries and bothers of life'.

A day's rest in bed has fallen out of favour as a folk remedy, but not so in hospitals, where sleep therapy – 'the balm of hurt minds' – is still regarded as a valuable form of treatment. Mentally sick patients who have failed to respond to orthodox treatment have been put to sleep with sedatives for several days at Montreal's Allan Memorial Hospital, being woken only for food, drink and essential toilet requirements. On this simple routine 57 per cent have shown either moderate or marked improvement. At Charing Cross Hospital, London, doctors have used deep-sleep treatment to tide coronary patients over the critical days immediately following their attack, when they might otherwise have been consumed by fear and shock. Using this sedative approach they reported only one death in their first fifty-nine cases, and that from a peptic ulcer rather than a second heart attack. In Russia prolonged sleep, induced by applying a low pulsating electrical current to the skull, has been successfully used to combat asthma, ulcerative colitis and a variety of skin disorders. The same treatment has been employed in Israel to cure cases of acute depression and anxiety.

113

Rest and sleep, far from being periods of idleness, are times of vital, recreational activity. The besetting sin of workaholics and Type A individuals is not that they work too much but that they rest and relax too little. Early this century Ivan Pavlov, the Nobel prize-winning Russian physiologist, demonstrated that even the strongest of animals will suffer a 'rupture' of nervous activity if they are subjected to long-continued stress.

Every year millions of words are written about stress – in newspapers, magazines and medical journals – and yet even today few people appreciate the distinction between short- and long-term stress. These stimuli have such totally different effects on the human body that they might well be considered separate entities. To accentuate this distinction they should perhaps be given different names, such as STS (short-term stress) and LTS (long-term stress).

STS is to be welcomed because it is exciting, pleasurable and life-enhancing. We enjoy the 'buzz' we get when our blood-streams are flooded with stress hormones. During these times we feel bright, think more clearly and perform more effectively. Research also shows that animals live longer when they are subjected to intermittent STS, because this develops the adrenal glands and keeps the neurohormonal defence mechanisms working at peak efficiency.

The problem today is not that we are being exposed to stress – which is as inevitable as growing old and as vital as eating and drinking – but that we too rarely get *relief* from stress. We are like soldiers kept constantly at the front line. To begin with we meet the challenge with heightened perception and improved perfor-mance but then, as the stimulatory effects of STS give way to the attritional changes of LTS, we experience a mounting exhaustion of our physical and mental reserves. Eventually we become 'shell shocked'.

Some people are more resistant to stress than others, but *all* will break down eventually if exposed to unrelieved LTS. This has been proved on the battlefield and also in internment camps when prisoners have been subjected to persistent 'brainwash-ing'. The dangers of LTS were confirmed when a psychiatrist studied 5,000 cases of battle fatigue arising during the course of the Second World War. 'All normal men eventually suffer combat exhaustion in prolonged, continuous and severe battle,' he reported. The same symptoms of battle fatigue can be observed in civilians when they are subjected to LTS.

We often make the mistake of regarding stress as a uniquely twentieth-century phenomenon. This may be true of LTS, but it certainly cannot be said of STS. Our forebears suffered stress which was often more intense than ours, but which rarely persisted. The approach of a sabre-tooth tiger subjected our ancestors to acute STS, during which their bodies were prepared for 'flight or fight'. But the crisis was quickly over. Either they clubbed the animal to death, they escaped to the sanctuary of their caves or they died a precipitous death from the beast's attack. This gave them no time to suffer a nervous breakdown or develop chronic hypertension or peptic ulcers. Not so today, when we are more likely to be subjected to non-stop work, incessant noise, ceaseless worry, long-continued pressures and unremitting emotional strain. This LTS provokes disease by upsetting the balance between the body's anabolic and catabolic processes.

History is replete with examples of men who performed enormous work-loads and shouldered heavy burdens of responsibility without obvious damage to either their well-being or health; because they achieved a better metabolic balance. Soldiers like Napoleon and Wellington had acquired the secret of relaxed endeavour. So too did statesmen like Churchill, Talleyrand and Kennedy, and creative geniuses like Edison and Alexandre Dumas. What was the secret of their equanimity? Each made a practice of taking regular healing retreats. When the pressure of work became excessive Talleyrand would take a few winks of sleep on his bed, telling his staff that he was 'going into conference'. When meetings at the White House reached an exhausting impasse President Kennedy would call a break, and while others took a cup of coffee or a cigarette he would rest his head on his desk and snooze. Wellington was another inveterate cat-napper and was discovered during the height of the Battle of Waterloo sleeping with a paper draped across his face to shield his eyes from the gunfire's flash.

Winston Churchill invigorated himself in a similar way. 'I have had recourse to a method of life which greatly extended my capacity for work,' he admitted. 'I always went to bed for at least one hour as early as possible in the afternoon.' Alexandre Dumas shared a similar secret. He often wrote through the night and thought nothing of dashing off an article while he was eating lunch. To maintain this frenetic pace he made a point of taking regular siestas. 'Often after my long nights spent working,' he wrote, 'when I have only had an hour or two's sleep, my eyes close and if I happen to be sitting near a wall, I rest my head on the wall, or if I am sitting at a table, my head falls on the table. Then, however awkward the angle my head makes with my body, I sleep for five minutes, and at the end of these five minutes I wake up sufficiently refreshed to start work again immediately.'

Tests carried out on university students show that individuals who take a post-lunch snooze remain fresher than those who soldier on without a break. The siesta was also found to improve their mood, reduce their feelings of anxiety, and quicken their reaction times. More recent research has shown that the afternoon rest may also reduce the risk of heart attacks. This was suggested by work carried out by Dr Dimitrios Trichopoulos of Athens University, who investigated a group of nearly a hundred men with heart disease and found that those who took an afternoon rest were considerably less likely to suffer a subsequent fatal heart attack.

But maintaining an attitude of repose means far more than finding time for regular spells of rest and recreation. To attain a state of optimum health we need to be mentally relaxed as well as physically rested. We need to achieve serenity of mind, emotional composure and a persistent and pervasive calmness of temperament. This sublime quality of equanimity is not easily developed, even by Buddhist monks living in the sanctuary of remote Tibetan monasteries. In the frenetic environment of a restless, crowded industrial city it is still less easy to attain.

We live in an age of global anxiety, a time when a highly developed communications industry unites to keep us in a state of constant alarm. We open the daily newspapers and read stories of brutal assaults and violent rapes. We watch the television and see harrowing pictures of starving children and brutalised soldiers. Our blood pressure rises when we read accounts of the torture of innocent political prisoners. Our hearts race when we see pictures of elderly people mugged for their meagre savings. Every hour of every day our bodies react to an endless succession of distress signals. Each time we are armed to fight the injustice or right the wrong. But the preparation for 'flight or fight' is purposeless, for the victims and villains of our media melodramas are invariably miles remote from our sphere of influence. So we remain fearful and frightened – but at the same time frustrated and unfulfilled.

Man, for all his civilised emancipation, remains essentially a group animal. In the wild it is easy to identify the group reactions of a flock of geese or herd of deer. Man's communal response to danger is less apparent but equally real. We may not take flight at the first hint of danger, like a pack of sheep, but behind our calm exterior we react empathically to the distress cries of our fellow human beings. When the world weeps for the victims of an earthquake, we too mourn. When the spread of terrorism makes the world fearful, we also suffer anxiety. When gratuitous cruelty to animals incenses the community, we share the same experience of anger.

We have grown so accustomed to this daily assault on our sensibilities that we do not realise how powerful and pervasive the emotional propaganda has become. If this point needs emphasising, take a copy of the most recent daily paper you have to hand. The first page you will find is reserved for international crises. Here there is no shortage of upsetting news – famines, wars, rebellions, hurricanes, air crashes, avalanches and earthquakes. Inside there will be fuller coverage of gruesome national tragedies – headless corpses, decomposing torsos, brutal muggings, suicides and child abuse. Even the country's economic events will be couched in terms designed to provide the maximum possible tension and distress. Strike-ridden factories will be described as 'doomed', political talks as 'battles', 'conflicts' or 'rows'. A temporary impasse in a round of wage-bargaining negotiations will be said to bring the talks 'near to collapse'; while a brief fall in share prices will be reported as giving the Stock Exchange 'the jitters'. This alarmist reportage serves to keep us in a constant state of free-floating anxiety, which is exaggerated by the regular circulation of doomsday predictions. One year we are asked to worry about the threat of nuclear war, the next about the hazards caused by pesticides, lead pollution, food additives, the AIDS epidemic or the growing hole in the ozone layer. We are suffering, not because we are exposed to greater *danger* than our forebears, but because we are exposed to greater *fear*.

A generation ago, before the advent of television and international news-gathering agencies, signals of distress had a purely parochial distribution. Throughout an entire lifetime a villager might have been involved in a handful of accidents, a few pub brawls, an occasional crop failure, one or two suicides and maybe a solitary murder. Now we live in a global village where these emotional traumas are our daily fare. The rapidity of the change becomes more obvious when one reflects that during the 1930s the BBC's news bulletins were liable to be cancelled for lack of news. On one occasion during this period the duty BBC announcer came on the air and said, as if it was an everyday occurrence: 'Good evening. Today is Good Friday. There is no news.'

Those days of parochial isolation are unlikely to return. As a result, since we now carry the cares of the world upon our shoulders as well as those of our personal milieu, it is more vital than ever that we should acquire the grace of equanimity. It is no use seeking relaxation on a Caribbean holiday if we take on the trip an anxious, harassed mind. In the same way little respite is gained from an afternoon's siesta, or even a full night's sleep, if the mind remains taut and tense while the body rests. Finding an escape from emotional tension seems to be a major preoccupation of the contemporary world, judging by the plethora of advertisements for spa baths, relaxation couches, herb pillows, vibrating beds, solaria, hammocks, calming stones, hand massagers and executive relaxation toys. But these relaxation aids are palliatives rather than cures. To overcome chronic tension and anxiety on a long-term basis we need cool hearts rather than hot baths. If we could acquire this emotional composure we would do far more to reduce the incidence of cardiovascular disease than by running marathons and existing on diets devoid of animal fats. This view is confirmed by Dr Irvine Page, a leading American heart specialist, who claims that the best way to avoid heart attacks is through the 'achievement of equanimity'.

That this is possible has been demonstrated by a major Coronary Prevention study financed by the US government. The three-year research project followed the lives of 800 men who had been the victims of previous heart attacks. Some of these men were given the conventional post-coronary counselling: reduce weight, stop smoking, eat less animal fat, take more exercise. Others were given psychological advice aimed at getting them to 'slow down, smell the roses and relax'. This behavioural re-conditioning programme proved a great success. Men who had previously been uptight discovered how to smile at life and laugh at themselves. Those who had always been engaged in a race against time learned to slacken their pace and enjoy themselves. Aggressive drivers began stopping at amber traffic lights and listening to taped music instead of getting irritated by traffic jams and slow drivers. The change lessened the strain on their hearts to such an extent that during the course of the study only 9 per cent of the men who received the behavioural training had suffered a recurrent heart attack compared with 19 per cent of those who had followed the conventional medical advice. This emphasises once again the relevance of adopting a healthy mental attitude, which stands out today as the single most important factor in the maintenance of health and the prevention of disease.

Several techniques can be used to acquire an attitude of calmness and equanimity:

- **Rest Pauses**
  *'A really efficient labourer,' said Thoreau, 'will be found not to crowd his day with work.' This balance between effort and repose, catabolism and anabolism, achieves the optimum level of performance with the least expenditure of energy and the smallest risk of generating tension and fatigue.*

In practical terms this means planning the day in such a way that time is provided for regular intervals of rest and quiet reflection. Entertainment, recreation and fun should become an integral part of the working day, rather than a bolt-on optional extra.

Convalescence is a therapy which should not be reserved for the occasional treatment of the sick, but which should be used as a daily tonic for the well. This is implied in the very origin of the word 'convalescence', which derives from the name of the ancient Roman bugle call which signalled troops to cease fighting and withdraw so that they could re-group their ranks and recover their strength before returning to the fray. We too need to step back from the firing line from time to time. These regular spells of recovery should be regarded as biological necessities rather than idle luxuries, for it is invariably the flat-out office worker who becomes the flat-out hospital patient.

• Holidays

Vacations can provide excellent opportunities for overcoming anxiety and learning to relax, providing they are suitably chosen. A century ago doctors selected holidays for their patients with the same care as they now prescribe drugs. Not so today, when holidays are planned with little thought for the physiological benefits they can provide. A recent American survey showed that only one in eight people intend to swim on their holidays, and more than a half have no plans to sunbathe. And yet vast numbers join the annual trek to the beaches. I wonder why?

Many people claim that they need the solitude that a holiday provides, and then join a coach party making a sightseeing tour around Europe. At the end of their whirlwind trip they return to their homes more tense and tired than when they left. The search for peace and quiet was one of the original reasons for taking a vacation, a word which stems from the Latin vacatio, which means both an emptying and a suspension of normal activities. This quietude is essentially a retreat into one's inner being, a stilling of body and mind which can be discovered in the remote wastes of a foreign countryside or in the peace of one's own back garden.

We need to take a vacatio from our everyday routines, responsibilities and worries – but this need not be a long, expensive trip. We could get the repose we need walking for one or two days in the local countryside, attending a weekend music festival or simply reading in a favourite fireside chair. We may experience peace of mind on an overseas annual holiday, but we must practise it at home in the course of our daily lives. This was the contention of Pascal who once said: 'The sole cause of man's unhappiness is that he does not know how to stay quietly in his room.'

The set-piece fortnight's holiday is a relatively recent invention, popularised by the travel trade because it is easy to package and sell. Prior to its arrival the majority of working people had to content themselves with breaks lasting no more than one or two days, associated with saints' days, festivals and public holidays. But these were allotted with considerable generosity. In medieval Britain the average farm labourer worked hard from dawn to dusk with only a Sabbath day of rest, but they knew that they could look forward to fifty-six days of annual holiday. The Egyptian peasants fared even better, for they were granted 150 holy days a year on which to worship their crocodile god. We would suffer less sickness if we too took our holidays in short, frequent breaks.

Professor Pierre Delbarre, of the Cochin Park Royal Hospital, Paris, is one of the few doctors in the world to have examined the medical implications of holiday-taking. He also stresses the benefits of brief, regular vacations. 'Biological imperatives' demand that we should take two or three periods of eight to ten days' holiday a year, he says.

One great virtue of a well-chosen vacatio is that it enables us to remain relaxed even when we return home and resume our everyday duties and cares. In recent years it has become possible to estimate the speed at which individuals unwind at the end of their working days, by measuring the rate at which their stress hormone levels fall. Some have been classified as 'slow epinephrine decreasers' because they find it difficult to 'switch off' and reduce their blood levels of the key stress hormone epinephrine (noradrenaline). Others have the ability to travel rapidly from a state of high arousal to one of mental and physical relaxation. These 'rapid epinephrine decreasers' are fortunate in that they *greatly reduce their daily load of stress. Trials carried out on a group of industrial workers revealed that the speed of unwinding increased for some while after the group members took a relaxing holiday. By taking short breaks at frequent intervals it is possible to make the most of this carry-over effect.*

*Brief holidays like this provide a natural convalescence cure, which is no doubt a major reason why the Japanese combine an exceedingly high rate of stress illness with the industrial world's poorest record for holiday-taking. (Japanese workers take only 60 per cent of their annual holiday entitlement.)*

- **Muscular Relaxation**
*Most people recognise the existence of a psychosomatic mechanism by which the mind influences the body; but few appreciate that there is also a somaticopsychic pathway, by which the body exercises control over the functions of the mind. This is particularly true of the link between the brain and the 656 muscles which form approximately 40 per cent of our total bodily weight. (The percentage is slightly higher for the average man and slightly less for the average woman.) When these muscles are tense, thousands of nerve impulses are transmitted to the brain informing it that the body is in a state of high arousal. It is as if a fire alarm were sounding in the skull, warning the brain to be ready for immediate action. This creates a sense of impending doom for as long as the state of tension lasts. Since there are many things today which make us tense, and few which necessitate the atavistic physical response of 'fight or flight', we often remain for hours on end in a condition of pent-up muscular tension.*

*One way to dissipate this tension and to switch off the cerebral klaxon horn, is to indulge in a spate of vigorous muscular activity. Children do this quite naturally to let off steam when, instead of fighting with their parents, they belabour their teddy bears or throw cushions around the room. In similar situations animals engage in what zoologists refer to as displacement activity. To burn off their tension herring gulls tug at tufts of grass and stags clash their antlers against a nearby tree. Man gets the same release by throwing temper tantrums or preferably felling trees, playing tennis or working in the garden. Teresa of Avila, the sixteenth-century Carmelite nun, was the founder of seventeen religious communities. She was a mystic, who advocated a life of contemplation, seclusion, prayer and fasting. Yet she also recognised the value of vigorous physical activity as a cure for unexpressed emotional tension. When any of her nuns showed signs of frustration she sent them into the garden to work. 'I have always found that the best thing for broody nuns is to make them dig,' she wrote.*

*A similar outlet can be obtained from activities like walking and gentle running, which provide socially acceptable methods of tension release. Their value was proved by experiments carried out by Dr Richard Driscoll, a Tennessee psychiatrist. He took a group of students suffering from pre-examination nerves and gave them a lengthy course of desensitisation training in which they were taught to relax while facing up to their fears. Other students, experiencing the same problem, were encouraged to take a gentle jog while concentrating their minds on pleasantly relaxing thoughts. Both therapies proved effective. As a result Richard Driscoll was forced to conclude in his report, published in* The Psychological Review, *that jogging was a simpler, quicker way of reducing anxiety than the far more cumbersome technique of progressive desensitisation. Others will relax without donning tracksuits or working up a sweat, by taking a brisk walk round the block. This was the technique favoured by Bertrand Russell, the philosopher, who was firmly convinced that 'unhappy businessmen would increase their happiness more by walking six miles a day than by any conceivable change of philosophy'.*

*A short-term escape from muscular tension can be obtained through massage and warm baths. A more permanent solution can be found by learning the art of physical relaxation. This technique – first described in 1938 by Dr Edmund Jacobson in his book* Progressive Relaxation *– has been used with success to lessen pain, to treat fears and phobias, to cope with examination nerves and to handle the worries of everyday life. The method demonstrates the effectiveness of the somaticopsychic approach, proving that peace of mind can be attained by establishing physical* *repose. By regular practice it is possible to trigger this sedative response as surely as by taking tranquilliser pills and almost as quickly as dousing a light. Equally important, by using this method it is possible to switch rapidly from complete repose to total arousal, a change which cannot be accomplished with chemical sedation, the effects of which persist for hours.*

*To acquire the knack of 'switching off' it is advisable to allocate 10 minutes a day for regular practice, preferably in a location where you are more likely to be free of noise and interruption. The exercises can be performed either lying down or when sitting comfortably in a chair. (The few moments before falling asleep in bed at night provide a perfect setting.) During these scheduled moments focus your attention on the various groups of muscles in your body – feet, legs, trunk, shoulders, arms and neck. Work progressively from feet to head and coax each area to relax, remembering that relaxation is a passive process which cannot be forced. Don't employ effort. Just give the muscles the suggestion that they are going to relax; then let it happen. Pay particular attention to the muscles of the hands, jaw and forehead, since these are the key areas where muscular tension is most commonly focused.*

*If to begin with you find it difficult to relax a particular muscle group, tense the region first and then let go, conjuring up the feeling that as the muscle relaxes it becomes increasingly limp, heavy and warm. The more you practise this exercise, the easier it will become to still the mind by bringing about a switch from a state of bodily tension to one of complete physical relaxation. Very quickly you will learn how to control your unwanted excesses of anger or anxiety. Instead of getting in a dither when you are waiting to give an after-dinner speech you will remain calm and composed by evoking the relaxation response. When you are driving a car and run into a traffic jam you will stay cool rather than get pointlessly irritated, by 'switching off' the tension signals which invite the brain to prepare for battle with traffic lights, road blocks and 'enemy' drivers.*

*In time the constant repetition of this practice will bring about a change in demeanour, making individuals who are normally* short-tempered and aggressive increasingly calm and equable. They will still be able to let their passions rage if they wish, but when this happens it will be a matter of conscious choice rather than an uncontrolled reaction to outside events.

Gains in health are also likely to follow training in physical relaxation. This was demonstrated by a team of workers from Ohio State University College of Medicine, led by Janice Kiecolt-Glaser, who gave thrice-weekly lessons in relaxation to a group of forty-five residents in a geriatric home. At the end of a month the old stagers reported an improvement in health not shown by a control group which had received 'social contact' visits but no specific relaxation counselling. Blood tests of the trained group also revealed a significant decrease in antibodies to the herpes simplex virus, which was taken as an indication of an improvement in their general immune system.

## • Hobbies

A change is often as good as a rest, especially when it involves a switch from work to a totally absorbing pastime or hobby. The person who is playing bridge may be concentrating intensely on the game, but they are certainly not worrying at the same time about their work or their marital problems. One television executive is an ardent model railway enthusiast which he finds an excellent antidote to stress. 'After a hard day I can switch on the trains and switch off the worries,' he reports. Many presidents of America and prime ministers of Britain have found a similar escape through fishing. This was the respite chosen by Herbert Hoover during the Great Depression. 'Presidents have only two moments of personal seclusion,' he reported. 'One is prayer; the other is fishing – and they cannot pray all the time.' Others induce a state of mental tranquillity when they knit, carve wood, cook, paint, arrange flowers or grow tomatoes. The ideal is to adopt leisure-time activities which provide a tranquil shelter from the storms of life. When used like this hobbies become productive remedies for killing anxiety rather than frivolous ways of killing time.

- ## Soothing Stimulation
  Hydrotherapists, masseurs, child psychologists and music therapists recognise that there are stimuli which provoke tension and
  others which induce tranquillity and relaxation. In general terms
  the relaxing stimuli are rhythmical and of low intensity, whilst the
  exciting stimuli are stronger and more abrupt. Water, depending
  on its temperature and method of application, can provide either
  effect. A dash of cold water on the face is a time-honoured way of
  reviving a fainting person, whereas a warm bath is an equally
  respected recipe for sedation. When masseurs want to produce
  stimulation they employ manipulations known as *tapotement*
  (hand percussion) and *petrissage* (kneading), which involve strong,
  vigorous handling of the tissues. If they want to encourage
  relaxation they utilise *effleurage*, which is a process of gentle
  stroking very similar to the soothing gestures a mother makes
  instinctively when she strokes the brow of a fretful child.

  These responses are inborn, for even the new-born child shows
  a strong inclination to be attracted by stimuli which are mild,
  rhythmical and slowly changing, and to be repelled by stimuli
  which are of a higher intensity and more abrupt rate of change –
  such as loud noises and rapidly moving objects. Practical use can
  be made of this physiological phenomenon in the treatment of
  tension states. The fractious infant can be rocked to sleep in its
  mother's arms. Disturbed children and the inmates of mental
  hospitals can find consolation by gently rocking their bodies.
  Jewish tradition acknowledges the same principle when it
  encourages mourners to comfort the bereaved by taking them in
  their arms and rocking them gently to and fro.

  Another related way of finding tranquillity is through the use of
  rocking-chairs. These made their appearance during the latter
  half of the eighteenth century, initially most probably as adap-
  tations of standard nursing chairs and then as purpose-built
  items of furniture. In America they found favour with many
  eminent men, such as Benjamin Franklin who popularised the
  Boston rocker, and Abraham Lincoln who gave his name to the
  Lincoln rocker. Later they were imported into England where they
  were marketed as 'American Common Sense Chairs . . . specially
  adapted for rest and comfort'. Their use encouraged quiet

reflection, an activity fostered by the inscription carved on the headpiece of many early models: 'Sit ye, Rock and Think'.

In recent years rocking-chairs have fallen out of favour, mainly because the world is now too busy to find time for quiet contemplation. Therein lies a sad paradox, for the more we pack our days with urgent business, the more urgently we need the therapy of quiet reflection. In North America attempts are being made to revive interest in the traditional rocking-chair. In Stamford, Connecticut, a club has been formed for rocking-chair enthusiasts, called the Sittin' Starin' 'n' Rockin' Club. And from Ontario, Canada, Dr R. C. Swan has published a medical paper on 'The Therapeutic Value of the Rocking-Chair' in which he extols the sedative virtues of rockers, a remedy which he claims is 'cheap and easily obtainable, has no side-effects, is non-toxic and needs no prescription'.

Music, when suitably chosen, offers another way of achieving calmness through soothing stimulation. The Old Testament provides what must be the earliest recorded example of musical psychotherapy, in the account of David playing his harp to lift the depression of King Saul. Since that time music has been regularly used to alleviate depression and cure states of agitation. 'Music has charms to soothe a savage breast,' observed the English poet and dramatist William Congreve. This was effectively demonstrated at Stoke City Football Club, Staffordshire, where outbreaks of crowd violence declined the moment the club stopped playing pop records before a match to whip up the fans' enthusiasm and switched instead to regaling them with soothing classical music.

Achieving effective sedation requires the correct blending of all three elements of musical composition – rhythm, melody and harmony. Not surprisingly, the basic musical beat, or *tempo moderato*, is set at the rate of the average heartbeat, which is the pre-eminent natural rhythm of human existence. (Babies sleep longer if they are exposed to the amplified sounds of their mother's pulse.) Music which is played at a quicker tempo than this, such as Scottish reels and Irish jigs, stimulates activity. Conversely, slower beats, like funeral dirges and nocturnes, encourage a mood of calm tranquillity. The principles of harmony *also follow fundamental physiological laws. Some combinations of notes we find soothing while others jar. Most people find it pleasing to combine two notes if the frequency of one is double that of the other (the octave above). Other generally appreciated harmonious combinations are provided by notes with frequencies in the ratio 4:5:6.*

*Although people's taste in music varies enormously, there is general agreement on the pieces which arouse and those which sedate. Two Italian obstetricians decided to provide music therapy in their labour ward. All but three of the thirty women to whom it was offered found it helped them during childbirth. When they needed to relax during the early stages of labour they opted for soothing melodies like the Chopin nocturnes or the Valse Triste of Sibelius. During the final, active stage they responded best to twist music or stimulating tunes like Rossini's William Tell overture. At the University of Jena, East Germany, psychiatric patients are helped to relax with the aid of soothing music. Here the most effective records have proved to be Handel's Largo and Bach's Air from the Suite in D Major.*

*The more frequently we listen to such music, the more we encourage a mood of equanimity. This is the civilising effect which Plato referred to when he wrote: 'Rhythm and harmony find their way into the inmost places of the soul, imparting grace and making the soul of him who is rightly musical, graceful.'*

* **Meditation**
*There are two commonly attempted ways of overcoming anxiety which nearly always fail. The first is to make the mind completely blank. This is a physiological impossibility, since only death can bring about a halt to cerebral activity. The second is to banish the cares and worries by a conscious effort of the will. This psychological battle rarely succeeds, for the more we try to forget a problem the more we make it the centre of attention. This is a paradox, a Catch 22 situation, which Professor Charles Baudouin, one of the scientific interpreters of Couéism, described as the Law of Reversed Effort. Insomniacs work themselves into a state of hyperarousal trying to stop their train of anxious thoughts.*

*Hypochondriacs make a great attempt to forget the rapid beating of their hearts, but the more effort they put into the task the faster and louder their hearts beat. Achieving equanimity is rather like catching an unruly puppy, the harder you chase it the more elusive it becomes.*

*A far more successful way of driving out anxious thoughts is to focus the attention on something which is intrinsically restful. This can be done by gazing at a flower or candle flame, listening intently to soothing music, or by reciting a poem or reading the 23rd Psalm. Providing the mind is filled with tranquil thoughts and feelings it will have no room for chronic cares. This meditative technique has been used for centuries in the East with outstanding success. Some years ago it was adopted by millions of people throughout the Western world in a simplified form known as Transcendental Meditation. By the regular chanting of a personal mantra, patients found that they could overcome insomnia, asthma, anxiety, chronic fatigue and drug addictions. Firms who gave their staff TM training claimed that it improved job performance, enhanced staff relationships, reduced tensions and increased job satisfaction.*

*Many disciples believed that their mantra cast a magic spell, but scientific research at the Thorndike Memorial Laboratory, Harvard University, has shown that the words or sounds themselves are immaterial. 'A similar technique used with any sound or phrase or prayer or mantra brings forth the same physiologic changes noted during Transcendental Meditation,' the researchers found. Some people undoubtedly find it easier to achieve a state of mental repose by repeating a meaningful phrase such as 'I am at peace with the world' or 'I am tranquil and serene'. Others will attain emotional equanimity by drawing or knitting. Watching the movements of fish can be equally soothing. This was demonstrated at the University of Pennsylvania when a group of students was set a complicated academic task which always produced an elevation of blood pressure. Given time the blood pressure subsided after the test, but the fall could be significantly accelerated by gazing at a tank full of tropical fish.*

*Another way to achieve equanimity is to fill the mind – not with restful sounds or sights, mantras or mandalas – but with peaceful* thoughts. This is the technique employed in Autogenic Training, the method of relaxation which draws its inspiration from the induction methods used by hypnotists. People who seek to relax by this method are encouraged to use their imagination to conjure up pictures of restful situations. Some may be advised to think of themselves lying in a meadow beside a peacefully moving stream. As they relax they hear the gentle rippling of the water, the sigh of the wind as it blows through the trees and the soothing trilling of the skylarks as they hover high above. In their mind's eye they visualise the soft green of the trees and the flowers which dot the fields with multi-coloured flecks. In their imagination they feel the warmth of the sun as it beats down on their body. Under its relaxing influence they feel their eyelids closing, their breathing growing slower and deeper and their limbs becoming increasingly heavy and warm. This is a simple method of inducing a state of physical and mental repose which can have a calming effect just as profound as that obtained by Transcendental Meditation.

This was demonstrated at St Mary's Hospital, London, where the technique was taught to a group of women undergoing treatment for breast cancer. Not surprisingly, many of the women before the trial were anxious and depressed. Others felt resentful and angry that their lives had been blighted by malignant disease, emotions which made them tense and readily fatigued. Then they were taught to relax their muscles, slow and deepen their rate of respiration and use their imagination to conjure up a peaceful scene of their own choosing. Once they achieved a state of greater repose their mood lifted. They became less anxious and depressed, their tiredness lessened and their energy increased. 'The simplicity of the imagery, suggesting a peaceful, pleasant scene', the report noted, 'meant that it was within everyone's grasp. Often the image made the patient smile, at a time when smiles were perhaps few and far between.'

Meditation can also improve our resistance to disease. This was demonstrated when the skin of an experienced meditator was injected with a chemical derived from the virus which normally causes shingles (Varicella zoster). At first the subject was told to behave quite normally, and for three weeks she was given *daily inoculations of the chemical followed by tests to assess her immune response. For the next three weeks the experiment was repeated in identical fashion, except that this time she was asked to meditate. The tests proved that this resulted in a significant improvement in her immune response, indicating that the mind has powers to modify our resistance to disease.*

*There are times when we cannot help coming into contact with infection or suffering emotional traumas, but there is never a moment when we cannot seek to control our imaginings and thoughts. By exercising this control we can make a profound difference to our mood, our energy levels, our susceptibility to infection and even our expectation of life. This was the power Thomas Hardy alluded to when he wrote: 'More life may trickle out of a man through thought than through a gaping wound.'*

## • Dispel Chronic Fears

*Far more people than is generally realised suffer chronic fears and phobias. A study of a group of 3,000 Americans showed that 41 per cent had an unwholesome fear of speaking in public, 32 per cent were afraid of heights and 22 per cent were terrified of insects. Others admitted to a dread of open spaces (agoraphobia), closed spaces (claustrophobia), blood (haematophobia), cats (ailourophobia), flying (acrophobia) or the dark (nyctophobia). These phobias are tiring and socially restrictive. They also present a major health threat, according to a study carried out by Dr A. P. Haines of University College, London, which showed that men who were afraid of heights, crowds or enclosed spaces were nearly four times as likely to suffer a fatal heart attack as those who did not suffer from chronic anxiety.*

*It is perfectly natural to experience fear as a reaction to an immediate threat to one's security. Muscles should tense when we confront a burglar, and the heart should pound a little quicker when we set fire to the kitchen curtains. Rapid responses like these prepare the body for instant action and are vital if we are to cope ably and quickly with dangerous situations. What needs to be avoided are the nagging anxieties and fears which have no* specific survival value – like unreasoned fears of strangers, arguments, spiders or the dark.

Professor John B. Watson, the pioneer of Behaviourist psychology, demonstrated that infants are born with only two innate fears – a fear of loud noises and a fear of falling or suffering a loss of support. All other fears, phobias and acute anxieties are acquired and established as chronic behavioural patterns through a process of constant repetition and reinforcement. Since these unfortunate psychic traits are learned, it follows that they can equally well be un-learned. Most irrational fears would disappear of their own accord if they were not constantly fed and watered. People who are shy expect to be embarrassed and socially maladroit whenever they meet strangers. Once this thought is implanted in their mind it becomes a self-fulfilling prophesy. True to their expectations they blush and stammer whenever they encounter someone new. This justifies their fear and makes it all the more certain that they will become tongue-tied the next time they find themselves in strange company.

To overcome these chronic anxieties psychiatrists often employ a technique known as Systematic Desensitisation, which gradually extinguishes the fear response. If a patient has a fear of cats they are invited to provide a table – known as a 'hierarchy of fears' – in which they list in order of severity their cat-related anxieties. At the bottom of the list they might place 'thinking about cats'; at the top 'holding a cat on my lap'. In between they might table 'looking at pictures of a cat', 'stroking a piece of cat fur', 'seeing a stuffed cat', 'watching a cat walking in the distance'. To overcome their ailourophobia they are encouraged to tackle their self-identified hierarchy of fears stage by stage. To begin with they train themselves to keep relaxed while looking at a photo of a cat, either by using tranquillisers or by practising the relaxation techniques described earlier in this chapter. When this stimulus no longer provokes a fear response they progress a stage further and repeat the process when they are stroking a piece of cat fur. So they progress until they can eventually handle a cat without becoming panic-stricken. In this way they gradually learn that cats are sources of delight rather than objects of fear.

Other psychiatrists prefer to tackle the problem by teaching patients coping skills. Tests show that whenever victims of arachnophobia come into contact with spiders they show a marked increase in their output of stress hormones, a fluctuation which is directly proportional to their assessment of their ability to deal with the anxiety-provoking situation. Research has shown that this potentially damaging stress response is attenuated when patients are given a feeling of heightened confidence and competence.

Another behavioural technique for overcoming human fears and phobias is equally effective in overcoming conditioned avoidance responses in animals, which have a very similar origin. A laboratory rat can be trained to avoid the light if it is given an electric shock whenever the lights are illuminated. In exactly the same way Professor John Watson produced a conditioned fear of mice in an eleven-month-old infant known as Albert B. Initially the babe enjoyed playing with mice. Then a loud noise was produced whenever a mouse was released in the child's room. Very quickly Albert came to associate mice with a fear reaction, and in this way a conditional anxiety response was established. (In Albert's case the apprehension was not limited to mice, but soon spread to embrace a fear of furry objects in general, including rabbits, dogs, sealskin coats, cotton wool and even the hair on Professor Watson's head!) Once created, these fear responses are exceedingly difficult to break, for the conditioned animal protects itself by avoiding the bright lights which cause it pain. In the same way the phobic child does its best to shun the mice which trigger off the frightening noise. In this way they reinforce their anxieties and never learn that there is nothing to fear from the bright light or furry animals.

To break this barrier, psychiatrists sometimes employ a technique of abreaction known as Implosion, in which they confront their patients with their specific fears for an hour or more at a time, first in fantasy and then in reality. In many cases this extinguishes the fear response in one or two months.

This is a modern application of the old folk treatment for anxiety, the principle of which was succinctly expressed by Ralph Waldo Emerson: 'Do the thing you fear and the death of fear is certain.' If we run away from our fears they will continue to haunt us, but if we face up to them they will disappear like ghosts in the night.

Pilots who survive a plane crash can easily develop a chronic terror of flying unless they put the fear to rout by making a quick return to the air. The earlier the hobgoblins of fear are put to rest the less chance they have to grow to frightening proportions. Military psychiatrists have started to employ this principle when they treat soldiers suffering from acute combat neurosis, and as a result have greatly reduced the toll of long-term psychiatric illness. In the First World War troops suffering from 'shell shock' were hospitalised and allowed to continue as psychiatric cripples. Now they are returned to the front line as quickly as possible, before their terrors have a chance to take root and grow.

During the Yom Kippur war of 1973 the Israeli army suffered practically one psychiatric casualty for every four men with physical wounds. To reduce this toll the army psychiatrists decided to introduce a 'face your fears' policy. Instead of sending shell-shocked men to convalesce in psychiatric hospitals they returned them to the battlefield as swiftly as possible. The change in treatment seemed callous, but has more than halved the incidence of long-term psychiatric illness. Now more than 60 per cent of disturbed men treated at front-line casualty stations are back in action within three days. Professor Noah Milgram at Tel-Aviv University explained the new approach to doctors who attended a symposium in that city. 'Take a man whose tank is hit and whose buddies are killed,' he said. 'If you send him back to hospital and treat him like a mental patient, the tank will continue to represent all the horrors he saw. If, on the other hand, you take him back to a tank, one with no corpses, he can learn to deal with what happened and carry on.'

We cannot expect to lead lives totally free of tragedy and disaster, but we can prevent these misfortunes from becoming a source of chronic anxiety. Worry is a habit which is acquired through constant reinforcement. As the Chinese say: 'You cannot prevent the birds of sorrow from flying over your head, but you can prevent them from building nests in your hair.'

As we think, so will we become. If we wish we can acquire the habit of worry or, if we prefer, we can establish the habit of calm equanimity. The choice is ours. If we take steps to banish our artificially acquired anxieties we can regain the composure and trust we had as infants, when we recognised only those two instinctive dreads – a fear of loud noises and a fear of falling. This would add to the serenity of our lives and substantially reduce the incidence of stress-related illness. This was Professor Watson's Utopian dream. 'Think how peaceful, how calm, how efficient our lives would be,' he mused, 'if we were no more fearful than the new-born baby.'

- ## Control Your Worries

The time most people spend worrying is generally enough, if properly applied, to eradicate the cause of their worries. Many people waste time worrying about the past, over which they have no control. Others spend time and energy worrying about the dreadful calamities they could encounter in the future, like the White Knight in Alice in Wonderland who always carried a mousetrap with him because, as he said, 'One never knows: I might have to catch a mouse some time.'

Worry has become one of the major preoccupations of the Western world. A survey of 9,000 Americans, carried out by the National Institute of Mental Health, suggests that 15 per cent of US citizens spend more than half their waking hours worrying. A land of wealth and freedom where 13 million adults are impoverished and imprisoned by anxiety neurosis. As a result of their morbid preoccupation they constantly sup the cup of woe, a gloom which is clearly displayed in their facial expressions. Because their brains are in a state of constant alarm they hold their bodies tense. They move with the jerky agitation of a drop of water landing on a red hot griddle. They take tranquillisers to calm their nerves, but remain sick and tired. They go on holidays to relax, but take with them their major cause of stress – their worrying inclination.

These individuals were not born tense, any more than people are born concert pianists or gifted painters, this was a habit they learned by constant practice. If they chose they could equally well acquire the art of calm composure. Two exercises in particular *help to break the worry habit. The first is to commit your concerns to paper, rather than to allow them to fester in your mind. This puts them into perspective and enables them to be tackled in an orderly sequence. This was the technique favoured by Winston Churchill during the tumultuous years of the Second World War, according to Lord Moran his personal physician, who recalled his encounters with Britain's wartime premier in his book* Winston Churchill: The Struggle for Survival. *Moran relates that on one occasion Churchill asked him if doctors knew much about the subject of worry. Then, before he had a chance to reply, the prime minister gave his own solution to the problem. 'It helps to write down half a dozen things which are worrying me. Two of them, say, disappear; about two, nothing can be done, so it's no use worrying; and two perhaps can be settled.' This is one simple way of keeping worrying within healthy limits.*

*Another is to schedule fixed worrying times. This is the technique favoured by Dr Thomas Borkovec, Professor of Psychology at Pennsylvania State University, who has investigated the problems of the fretful sufferer and established the Pennsylvania Worry Group. He advises his clients to set aside a regular time and place for worrying. During the rest of the day they can jot their problems down in a notebook, after which they must school themselves to switch their attention to something more enlightening – the completion of an unfinished task or a walk around the park. Then, when their 30-minute 'worry period' arrives, they are free to wallow in their problems, solving those they can and burying the rest for consideration at a later date. In this way they gradually learn to reduce the time they spend in worry, from five or more hours a day to a maximum of thirty minutes. This is a particularly valuable discipline for twilight insomniacs, who stir in the small hours of the morning and keep themselves awake by churning over their problems. They should keep a pad by their bedside where they can list their anxieties for consideration during their next 'worry period', for as Harold Wilson observed during his premiership of Britain: 'If the problem that is keeping you awake is not soluble at 9 am it is certainly not soluble at 3 am, when you are feverish, neurotic, half asleep and just plain daft.'*

*People who follow this tip invariably find that their worries shrink when they are made the focus of their attention. This follows a process psychologists call 'extinction', which applies to all strongly repeated stimuli. If you live by the sea you soon adapt to the noise of the crashing waves. If you wear clothes throughout the day you rapidly cease to react to their pressure on your skin. In exactly the same way if you worry intensely for five or ten minutes your problems will quickly lose their power to excite and will begin to seem mundane, trivial or even ludicrous.*

*Or, if you prefer, you can try the technique the Koreans use to dispel their worries. They list their troubles on little slips of paper which they fix to the tail of their kites. Then, when their kites are flying high in the sky, they cut their tethering strings so that their troubles drift away into space.*

*Tricks like these may seem ridiculous to the inveterate worrier, but they do undoubtedly work. However anxious we are – by nature or by nurture – we can exercise conscious control over our fretful thoughts. This was proved at the University of California, when students were shown a disturbing film of workers sustaining horrendous injuries in a carpentry workshop. On some occasions they were asked to detach themselves from the emotional impact of the film; at other times they were asked to empathise with the victims. In every case they were left to control their own emotional responses, with no advice on how they could detach themselves from the suffering or identify with the injured victims. A measurement of their heart rates showed that even without instruction they could control their reactions to a significant extent.*

A far better degree of emotional control can be attained by people who adopt the techniques listed in this chapter. As the behaviourists have shown there is no such thing as a *born* worrier. Equally well there is no such entity as an *incorrigible* worrier. By patient practice everyone can acquire an attitude of mental calm. Pollyanna, the heroine of Eleanor Porter's novel, found her habitual peace of mind by repeatedly seeking four good things in every adverse happening. Ruskin suggested that serenity could be cultivated by building up a treasure house of restful thoughts:

'Bright fancies, satisfied memories, noble histories, faithful sayings . . . which care cannot disturb, nor pain make gloomy, nor poverty take away from us.'

By these various techniques we can learn to overcome the habit of non-productive worry and acquire peace of mind.

Chapter Ten:

# CONFIDENCE
## The Third b-Attitude of Health

People with low self-esteem have been found to have an above-average chance of contracting diseases of the heart and lungs. They are also more liable to develop auto-immune disease and to suffer rapid progression of malignant growths. This increased predisposition to disease is probably caused by stress, since the person who feels inadequate also feels incapable of coping with the problems they face. This is confirmed by blood tests which reveal that people with weak psychological defence mechanisms have higher levels of circulating stress hormones than those with greater self-confidence.

At one end of the scale of self-assurance there are the timid, inadequate individuals whose health is constantly below par. At the other extremity there are the schizophrenics who harbour delusional ideas about their strength and power. These misguided paragons are known to have an exceptionally low risk of contracting stress-related sickness. They *think* themselves to be omnipotent, an attitude not based on reality but one which nevertheless enables them to enjoy a remarkable record of health. Tests show that these super-confident individuals are highly tolerant to pain and surgical shock, have a lower-than-average risk of developing arthritis and allergies and possess a high resistance to most infections. (Tuberculosis is the one reported exception to this rule.)

In the fight against disease what matters is not simply the *objective* measurement of our physical health, but also our *subjective* estimate of our ability to cope. Better a confident 'weakling' with puny frame and sagging torso than a neurotic athlete with powerful chest and rippling muscles.

The greater our self-assurance and feeling of personal worth, the greater our resistance to disease and the greater our chance of achieving happiness and peace of mind. The fact that schizophrenic patients have an above-average level of well-being underlines the importance of the laws of psychogenic health, which are ignored by the vast majority of their 'sane' countrymen. No wonder some manic patients prefer to live with their delusions of grandeur than face a world of mediocre, sick 'normality'. As one said when told that he was cured and going to be discharged from his psychiatric hospital: 'Yesterday I was Napoleon, now I'm nobody.'

Somewhere there lies the happy mean between reasonable self-assurance and unwholesome pride and self-aggrandisement. This balance between confidence and conceit, humility and self-abasement, is not easy to strike as Benjamin Franklin found. He had a tendency to intellectual arrogance which he tried to curb but, as he confessed in his diary, he felt sure that even if he succeeded in conquering his pride for a while he would almost certainly relapse after a few days and become proud – of his humility! But it is far better to have a justifiable pride in one's appearance, abilities and achievements, as Franklin had, than to make life one long apology for real or imagined shortcomings and deficiencies.

Many people are crippled by an inferiority complex. They are so pathologically unsure of themselves that they constantly need the approval of others to bolster up their fragile egos. In this they are like the nymphomaniacs and Don Juans who engage in a ceaseless round of sexual encounters in a futile attempt to reassure themselves of their desirability and sexual potency. But the only confidence worth having comes from within. What matters is not the estimate that other people have of our personal worth, but how we value ourselves. 'No one can make you feel inferior without your consent', was Eleanor Roosevelt's way of summarising the situation. We cannot love others unless we have learnt to love ourselves. We cannot trust others if we have no trust in ourselves. And we cannot expect to feel comfortable in the company of others unless we first learn to be relaxed and happy in our own company.

People who develop this inner assurance can go about their daily tasks without having to worry about their public image. Since they are content to be themselves they do not need to maintain a false façade, nor do they have to surround themselves with status symbols to bolster up their feeling of importance and worth. As a result they are more gentle, contented and relaxed. Heavyweight boxers are often the mildest of men in public because they do not need to resort to aggressive displays and fisticuffs to prove their strength. Similarly, men of real genius are generally so assured of their ability that they do not need the constant approval of the crowd. Like Cato the Elder, who cautioned a friend who complained that no statue had been erected in Rome to honour his work as statesman and philosopher. 'No,' said Cato, 'I would rather have people ask "Why isn't there a statue to Cato?" than "Why is there one?" '

Man, unlike most other mammals, enters the world in a state of total dependence – incapable of walking or even standing erect. From this position of utter helplessness the human infant struggles to achieve a growing measure of autonomy. Many youngsters find it exceedingly difficult to undergo this weaning process. Regrettably for some the transition into adult independence is never complete. Whether through their physical weakness, smallness of stature, childhood illness or overprotective parental upbringing they find it easier to maintain their dependency on others. As a result, even though they grow to be six foot tall and rise to occupy responsible positions at work, they still remain immature children at heart.

Some cultures actually foster this continuing dependence. This is particularly true of the Japanese who decry any show of individuality and discourage any expression of independent activity. In the discipline of their children they encourage the inculcation of a character trait known as *amae*, which embraces passive dependence and an unquestioning subservience to everyone in a position of authority, irrespective of their intrinsic ability. This early training in self-effacement prepares the young Japanese for a life in which loyalty to a group – family, university or firm – always takes precedence over the expression of the ideas or beliefs of the individual. Any Jap who offends this social code by being self-assertive suffers loss of face and shame. These uniquely oriental punishments are so powerful, and can produce so great a loss of self-esteem, that some Japs resort to suicide as the only way of purging the group of their unworthy selves.

This is in contradistinction to the upbringing of the Jewish child, who is actively encouraged by his parents to become a juvenile prima donna. Here the desirable trait is not *amae* but *chutzpah*, a delightful Yiddish word which defies exact translation but which embraces a blend of audacious cheek and good-humoured self-assertion. It is this quality of pride and daring self-confidence which enables a Jewish lad to walk up to the prettiest girl at a party to ask for a dance, or knock on his boss's door after his first week at work to request a hike in salary. This difference in cultural training explains why excessive shyness is more common in Japanese than in Jewish youngsters. This was confirmed by a survey carried out by Philip Zimbardo, Professor of Social Psychology at Stanford University, which showed that *five* times more Japanese children complained of suffering chronic shyness than American children.

Modesty can be endearing, but extreme shyness can be a crippling psychological illness leading to social isolation, under-achievement and morbid introspection. Lack of self-confidence also causes stress when we are plunged into situations when we fear that our inadequacies and embarrassment are likely to be exposed. This frequently occurs when we are speaking in public or meeting people of high social rank. Studies show that when we are talking with our peers we experience a modest increase in blood pressure, but when we converse with someone whom we judge to be of a higher social status, our blood pressure leaps dramatically. In these situations we become tense and socially maladroit. One effect of this gaucheness was expressed by the portrait painter who was so tongue-tied when he was introduced to the Queen that when asked if he had any brothers he came out with the delightful malapropism: 'No Sam, but I've got two misters.' When placed in these stressful positions the chronically shy should remind themselves that they are not dealing with an Olympian god but with a human being who possesses the same frailties as they have, and the same complement of brain cells activating an identical number of arms and legs. This was Montaigne's thought when he wrote: 'Perched on the loftiest throne in the world we are still sitting on our own behind.'

During my days in practice I have been privileged to treat people of all ranks and stations of life, from builders' labourers and refuse collectors to cabinet ministers, international film stars and members of the royal family. At first I used to stand in awe of my VIP patients, which affected the ease with which I handled them. Then I realised that their needs and problems were no different from those of all my other patients. What's more I discovered that great or small they all looked the same in their underclothes! Nudity is the great social leveller, and doctors find it easy to cut their haughty patients down to size by the simple expedient of asking them to strip.

If we are to lead healthy, effective lives we must achieve a reasonable measure of self-assurance – at the earliest possible age. This was demonstrated by research workers at the University of Minnesota, who examined a number of pre-school infants and divided them into two groups according to their personality characteristics. The first group consisted of youngsters who exhibited a high level of anxiety and close attachment to their mothers; the other of toddlers who were more independent and secure. The behaviour and achievement of the children was then assessed as they progressed through school, both by their teachers and also by a team of independent observers, who were not told the findings of the initial groupings. The observers made their assessments independently, yet they showed a remarkable degree of consistency. The children who had been placed initially in the self-assured category scored on every count. They showed greater qualities of leadership, more flexibility and a greater willingness to confront opportunities and challenges. In their relationships with their classmates they showed greater empathy and they themselves were judged by their fellows as being especially attractive. In addition they had a higher level of self-esteem, which was accompanied by enhanced social skills and a higher level of emotional well-being.

These social attributes help a child to make friends and influence people. They also equip them to cope with the vicissitudes of later life. We never know when disaster will strike. Tomorrow we could be involved in a burglary, a motorway crash or a hotel fire. How well we emerge from these catastrophes depends in part on our physical fitness, training and equipment, but far more so on our strength of personality. This is the opinion of survival expert Martyn Forrester. In his book *Survival* he suggests techniques for dealing with most of the extremities of physiological distress. To prevent hypothermia in sub-zero temperatures he recommends padding one's outer garments with dry grass and leaves. To fight starvation when stranded in barren countryside he suggests a diet of caterpillars and worms. To cope with thirst in the desert he provides instructions for constructing a solar still. The timely use of these ingenious emergency drills can save lives, but they are of far less value than determination and self-confidence. According to Forrester: 'The single most important rule that anyone could teach you about the business of staying alive: *you'll survive if you think you can.*'

These qualities of rugged self-reliance are among the most valuable legacies we can bequeath to our sons and daughters. We cannot shield our children from the fires of adversity, but we can give them the strength of will to come through the flames unscathed.

Children are extremely hardy animals and can withstand all manner of hardships – sickness, poverty and malnutrition – providing they have a healthy attitude of mind. This was demonstrated when research workers Emmy Werner and Ruth Smith carried out a remarkable twenty-year study of children growing up in Kauai, a deprived area of Hawaii. The children were raised in conditions of chronic poverty by parents who had little formal education. They were exposed to higher-than-average rates of premature birth and infection. Many came from broken homes or one-parent families. Yet some survived these early stresses to become able, successful, socially confident adults, who 'worked well, played well, loved well, and expected well'. Their story is told in *Vulnerable, But Invincible*, in which the two research workers describe the qualities of the 'resilient' children, who formed one-in-ten of the total group. What enabled this small élite band to survive their early tribulations, when most of their playmates fell by the wayside? According to the survey, which followed the children from before their birth to their early twenties, the outstanding characteristic of the survivors was that they had 'a more positive self-concept, and a more nurturant, responsible, and achievement-oriented attitude towards life'. This confidence and independence was established at a very early age, according to the researchers, who comment on the 'advanced self-help skills and autonomy noted among these children in their second year of life'.

There is a tendency today to think of stress as an inevitably harmful and unwelcome intrusion in our lives. In fact it should be greeted as an exciting, life-preserving stimulus. It is true that stress can be a killer if it is allowed to run amok, but medical research has proved beyond doubt that if it is handled wisely it can add years to life and life to years.

Psychogenic illness arises only when the challenges we encounter exceed our coping skills, or more accurately when they exceed our *estimate* of our ability to cope. This was shown when social psychologists studied executives of the Illinois Bell Telephone Company at a time when the organisation was passing through a period of unprecedented upheaval and change. Two hundred of the managers surveyed were judged to be experiencing a high level of stress. Half of these had broken down under the pressure of work and were suffering definite illness, while the remainder flourished. As far as could be detected there was no difference in the situation and life-styles of the two groups. They shared similar ages, incomes, educational attainments, job status and ethnic backgrounds. What was it that enabled some of the executives to cope unscathed with a very high level of stress, while many of their equally able colleagues succumbed? Careful analysis revealed that the secret lay in their healthier attitude of mind. The survivors were protected by a mental quality which the researchers described as 'hardiness'. They had a strong sense of personal commitment and a great confidence in their ability to control their lives and the misfortunes that befell them. This was combined with a tendency to view stressful situations as challenges rather than threats. It was this self-assurance which gave them the peace of mind to enjoy the good times and the strength of character to endure the bad times.

To avoid anxiety we need to feel in control of our lives. This is particularly true of the inmates of concentration camps, who can avoid being brainwashed providing they retain a measure of control over their situation. Some prisoners have achieved an illusion of independence by inviting guards into *their* cells; others by following a policy of passive resistance, by which they affirm that even when they are operating under duress they will do things in *their* chosen time and in *their* preferred manner. This was the technique used by Nathan Sharansky, the Soviet-Jewish dissident, during his nine-year internment in Russian prisons and labour camps. To assert his independence he would turn left when his guards ordered him to turn right. To exert pressure on the Russian authorities he went on hunger strike. 'If you want to remain a free man, if you don't want to become a laboratory rat in the hands of the KGB *you must resist*,' he said. 'Every time you insist on your views, defend your actions . . . you prove to yourself that you haven't surrendered to fear, and that *you* are the master of your fate.'

Experiments show that the health of laboratory animals suffers if they are placed in a contrived situation where they are made to feel helpless or hopeless. This applies to rats, chickens, monkeys and even cockroaches. The same is true of humans who become depressed when life seems drained of hope. Others lose their will to live if they imagine that they are the hapless victims of fate, a decline which has been described as 'submissive death'.

Dr Bruno Klopfer is also convinced that there is a close association between tumour spread and lowered self-esteem. He has used personality tests to determine whether cancers would develop slowly or rapidly, and has achieved a predictive accuracy rate approaching 80 per cent. When people are insecure, he conjectures, they tire themselves out and lower their resistance by maintaining a constant struggle to cope with their anxieties and inadequacies. 'If, however, a minimum of vital energy is consumed in ego-defensiveness, then the cancer has a hard time making headway.'

Scientists at first may find it difficult to accept these airy theories, and yet they *are* supported by carefully controlled laboratory tests which reveal a link between helplessness, immune response and cancer growth in animals. In one set of experiments a group of rats was given a mild electric shock, which they were trained to control by operating a simple on/off switch. Another group received the same strength shock at the identical time, but were given no means of escape from the mildly painful pricks. Blood tests showed that the rats receiving the uncontrollable shocks suffered a deterioration in their immune response. This impairment in their normal defence against infections, foreign bodies, allergies and cancer cells was not found in the other rats which were similarly stressed, but retained the power to control their fate.

There is little doubt that this biological response to 'helplessness' can increase the risk of cancer growth, at least in laboratory animals. This was confirmed by another series of tests, in which tumorous cells were injected into rats, which were then subjected to either controllable, or uncontrollable stress. Once again it was the 'helpless' animals which were found to be at greatest risk. Among the group receiving the uncontrollable shocks only 27 per cent proved strong enough to repel the tumour; a much poorer performance than the rats who were able to control their situation and who managed to reject the cancer cells in 63 per cent of cases.

Unlike rats, human animals have an enormous potential for controlling their environment – *providing they choose to exercise that power*. Many things can subject us to stress – noise, work, people, situations, bank overdrafts, overcrowded living conditions – but all these annoyances are subject to our control. If we are exposed to excessive noise we can move to the country or insulate our homes with soundproof doors and double-glazed windows. If our work is uncongenial we can change jobs. If we are pressurised by money worries we can institute economies to help us live within our means. If our marriages are unhappy we can seek marital counselling, compensate by taking up a range of outside activities, or seek a divorce. Even if we are lost on a mountainside, or clapped in prison, we can exercise a high measure of control over our destiny. In the vast majority of cases, even when we are subjected to severe stress, we are in the happy position of the autonomous rats in the psychologists' experiments, in that we can invariably control our fate by turning the master switch. If we don't like the cards we are given we can always reshuffle the pack and deal ourselves another hand. Yet in practice we often react like the 'helpless' rats in the laboratory tests, either because we refuse to exercise our freedom of choice or because we are too timid to make the behavioural choices that are open to us.

Ideally the priceless gift of self-assurance should be bestowed in early infancy. When it is not, it can be acquired in later life, slowly and painstakingly, by observing the following rules:

- ### Accept Full Responsibility for Your Life
  *Confidence can never be acquired until we learn to accept personal responsibility for both our actions and the outcome of our actions. Only then can we say with the absolute conviction of the Victorian poet W. E. Henley: 'I am the master of my fate; I am the captain of my soul.' Too often we prefer to blame others for our failures. We may point to a broken home to excuse our emotional insecurity. We may claim that we are not gaining promotion at work because we have a prejudiced boss. We are putting on weight because we are provided with over-rich food at home. We have not developed our artistic skills because we are too busy earning a living. These are lame excuses to cover our shortcomings. If we were honest we would admit that we have the power to gain promotion, lose weight or learn to paint – if we choose to use it.*

  *Too often we try to lean on others in the hope that we can shed the onerous responsibility of self-determination. We make the maintenance of our health the duty of doctors. We commit the upbringing of our children into the hands of educationalists. We delegate to the state the task of caring for us in our old age, expecting social-service agencies to provide us with pensions, welfare benefits and comfortable retirement homes. If we become hooked on drink or drugs we look for experts to provide us with a quick-fire cure for our addiction. If we are depressed, bankrupt or unemployed we expect to find specialist helpers to drag us from the mire. But if we rely too much on outside aids – specialists, counsellors and welfare agencies – we sacrifice our independence.*

*Lawyers, doctors and financial consultants can provide us with invaluable specialist advice, but they cannot, and must not, be given the final responsibility for governing our lives. If we are to achieve a state of healthy autonomy, we must rely on our own resources. Like waterfalls we must channel our own paths. This independence of spirit is one of the signs of mental health and also one of the hallmarks of greatness. After all, did the Rothschilds ask the advice of investment analysts every time they bought a line of stock? Did Napoleon consult the stars before he embarked on the battle of Marengo? Did Abraham Lincoln need a team of script-writers to draft the Gettysburg address? Did John Bunyan call on psychiatrists to lift him from the Slough of Despond? These men succeeded because they knew that these tasks were their responsibility and theirs alone.*

*The acknowledgement that we are the masters of our fate is the first step in the attainment of self-assurance. This courageous acceptance of the total responsibility for life's achievements and failures was well stated by Bernard of Clairvaux, the twelfth-century French saint and theologian, who wrote: 'No thing can work me damage but myself; the harm that I sustain I carry about with me; and I am never a real sufferer but by my own fault.'*

- **Be Yourself**
  *In order to become self-assured, we must first develop a well-defined feeling of self. Some men try to assert their individuality by wearing monogrammed shirts and driving a car with personal-*

ised number plates. Others attempt to prop up their identities with a scaffolding of status symbols. But a strongly based sense of personal identity cannot be cobbled from artefacts like these.

The main reason why we resort to these tricks is that we find it easier in today's amorphous society to identify what is 'mine', than to arrive at a clear-cut understanding of what is 'me'. So we base our identities and self-esteem on the jobs we hold, the clothes we wear, the cars we drive and the money we own. But the more we place reliance on these external trappings the less sure we become of our own intrinsic worth and real identity. This danger has been exposed by psychoanalyst Eric Fromm in Man for Himself, who points out that our great problem today is not that we are preoccupied with our selves, but that we have too little interest in our real selves and too much concern for the outward symbols of self.

This self-effacement is encouraged in vast industrial societies where the emphasis is placed on the welfare and image of the group rather than the interests and identity of the individual. For its own protection modern Western society favours the conformist, the citizens who say what they are brought up to say, who do what their superiors want them to do, who believe what the state wants them to believe, who go where their firms direct, and who behave in the way their neighbours expect. This makes them predictable, interchangeable and easy to handle.

Because we live in tight communities and closely integrated working groups we find it difficult to accommodate eccentrics and mavericks who refuse to fit into the pigeon-holes that society has constructed for them.

We train our children to fit the twentieth-century mould. But while contemporary society encourages conformism, psychiatrists argue the case for a more rugged individualism. This, they say, is the way to freedom, contentment and self-fulfilment, a doctrine which has the support of the world's great religious leaders. Buddha told his disciples: 'Be ye lamps unto yourself. Be your own reliance. Hold to the truth within yourself as to the only lamp.' Shakespeare expressed the same thought when he wrote: 'This above all; to thine own self be true. And it must follow as night the day that thou cans't not be false to any man.'

In order to achieve this autonomy we must learn to make our own independent decisions, without being swayed by outside opinion. This can be difficult to do initially, since we are trained from childhood onwards to avoid interpersonal disagreement. This was revealed by a remarkable experiment conducted by social psychologist Solomon Asch. He asked a group of university students to look at lines of varying length and then match them with a line of identical length selected from a choice of three alternatives. The visual discrimination was fairly easy to make and the students were able to match the lines with almost perfect accuracy when they were working on their own. Then the researchers resorted to a subterfuge to cloud their judgement. Into the test room they introduced other students who were ostensibly invited to carry out the same test, but who were actually confederates asked deliberately to falsify their responses. This had a disastrous effect on the performance of the original students, whose judgement began to falter the moment they found their opinions conflicting with those of the new arrivals. Instead of adhering to their own estimates, three-quarters began to be influenced by the falsified assessments of those around them. As a result their scores plummeted. Even when the majority view was grossly and obviously inaccurate, many still preferred to go along with the crowd rather than back their own judgement.

This is a sad indictment of modern education, which is producing youngsters with academic skills who lack the courage of their convictions. Instead of training them *how* to think, we are teaching them only *what* to think. So they are growing up without confidence in their personal judgement. Instead of acting as individuals they are in danger of becoming clones, dressing as others dress, enjoying books that others admire and following crazes and cults that others create. Even their freedom to enjoy a joke appears to be severely conditioned by the audience they are with. This was demonstrated at Cardiff University, when subjects were invited to watch a series of taped comedy programmes. When they were on their own they found the programmes funny, but their laughter was inhibited when they were with people who were not equally amused.

151

We can never lead relaxed, secure, independent lives if we are constantly looking over our shoulders to see what others are thinking and doing. Nor can we achieve autonomy if we are dishonest with ourselves. So many people lead lives of quiet deception, trying to conform with the expectations of their parents, neighbours or friends. As a result they are like actors, constantly wearing a mask and forever playing roles devised by someone else. But the word 'individual' comes from the same early English root as the word 'indivisible'. It refers to a person who is undivided and unique rather than someone who is undifferentiated, two-faced or a mass-produced replica of the populace at large.

Psychologists find that people frequently suffer stress when they struggle to maintain a false public image as a hero, screen goddess or great lover. They call this the 'impostor phenomenon', a syndrome to which we are all exposed if we seek to live a lie. Far easier to be our original selves than to try to be a carbon copy of someone else. And we are unique; to an extent to which few of us can even begin to comprehend. Even our individual cells differ from those of every other mortal who has ever lived. Each one contains more than 50,000 genes, with countless genetic units of DNA. This means that the cells of any two non-related individuals are likely to show as many as 10 million differences. Our cosmic responsibility is to express this individuality.

This we can do if we set our own standards and lead our own lives. Diogenes, the ascetic Greek philosopher, is reputed to have lived in a barrel. Certainly he was not a wealthy man, but he did have his independence which he prized more highly than material possessions. On one occasion he was chided by Aristippus, another philosopher: 'If you would only learn to flatter the king, you would not have to live on such poor food as lentils.' To which Diogenes replied: 'If you had learnt to live on such food as lentils you would not need to flatter the king.' Like Diogenes, we achieve independence by learning to live within our resources, and not by maintaining a dependence on outside aid.

If we are totally reliant on modern technology we will be especially vulnerable to power cuts and rail strikes. If we place our trust in money, we are at the mercy of fluctuations in stock-

*market prices and rates of currency exchange. If our health depends on the products of pharmaceutical science we will be dumbfounded if we find that their drugs bring us iatrogenic sickness rather than freedom from disease. If we lead our lives according to the tenets of psychological gurus we will flounder without guidance if their doctrines prove to be meaningless mumbo-jumbo. The fewer our dependency needs, the greater our security. The more we are willing to be ourselves, the greater our contentment. This is the yardstick by which our health will be measured and our lives judged.*

*Rabbi Zusia, the Chassidic mystic, expressed this principle with great simplicity when he said: 'When I die, God will not ask me why I was not Moses. He will ask me why I was not Zusia.'*

## • Set Reasonable Goals

*If we set ourselves unrealistic goals we invite failure, which in its turn creates despondency and loss of self-esteem. If on the other hand our targets are more appropriate to our abilities, and we succeed in achieving them, we gain immediate satisfaction and long-term self-assurance. This produces a snowball effect, in which success breeds success in ever-widening layers. Psychologist William James recognised this process at the turn of the century, when he postulated that an individual's level of Self-Esteem could be measured as the product of their Achievements divided by their Expectations.*

*We will suffer Angst if we cannot liberate ourselves from the desires and demands we know we cannot satisfy. As indicated in the chapter on Commitment, the art of personal fulfilment is to make a bouquet with the flowers within our grasp.*

## • Establish Control Over Your Environment

*When we are in situations we cannot control we invariably experience a measure of anxiety. This is why it is often more comfortable to give than to receive, because while we are dispensing affection and help we retain total control of the situation. This autonomy is sacrificed when we are on the receiving end of the* transaction, since then we become dependent on the continuing goodwill of our benefactors. Stress also arises during periods of uncertainty, when we again feel doubtful of our ability to control the course of events. This antipathy towards the unknown is shown by institutions as well as individuals. It is often said in financial circles that the stock markets of the world can stand anything – but uncertainty.

We are happier and healthier when we feel in reasonable control of the world around us. The development of this inner confidence and composure is an essential part of the schooling provided by Shyness Clinics in America, where clients are encouraged to overcome their diffidence through a programme of assertion training, role-playing and social-skill tuition. The success of these classes depends on the acceptance of certain basic principles, the chief of which according to the Stanford University Shyness Clinic are:

* You have control over what you feel and do
* You are responsible for those feelings and actions and for creating the consequences you want

However bashful and ineffectual people may feel to begin with, if they adopt these maxims, and act on them, they will gain a gradually increasing confidence in their ability to master their immediate environment. This process of behavioural re-education is generally a far more effective way of building self-assurance than conventional psychoanalysis and psychotherapy, which tend to favour dependence on the therapist rather than the development of the autonomy of the client. Even the language therapists use encourages the development of a dependent, parent/child relationship. This was shown by a study which revealed that psychologists and psychiatrists use five times as many words implying 'passivity' and 'being acted upon' as those which suggest 'action' and 'self-steering behaviour'.

If we are to attain the beneficial mental attitude of self-assurance we must constantly emphasise our independence and autonomy – in the words we use, the thoughts we entertain, the deeds we perform and the relationships we establish. This is vital in the fight against cancer, as Lawrence LeShan proved when he revealed the close link between the onset of malignant growths and the harbouring of feelings of 'helplessness' and 'hopeless-ness'.

This rugged independence is also crucial if we want to die young, at the latest possible age. Morton Lieberman, a University of Chicago psychologist, studied the fate of a group of over eighty elderly people who were admitted to three local homes for the aged. Although their ages ranged from sixty-three to ninety-one, they were all in good physical and mental health at the time of their admissions. Yet several died within a few months of losing their independence and becoming institutionalised. Of the remainder, all but 30 per cent suffered a marked decline in health within a year of entering a geriatric home. What were the pre-eminent features of this small band of hardy veterans, who showed a quick and healthy adaptation to their new conditions? According to Lieberman, the 'survivors' were characterised by their high levels of self-esteem. They were also outstandingly active, autonomous and self-assertive, personality traits which made it easier for them to withstand the turmoil of change and cope with the pressures of institutional life.

- Gain Experience
  Like most other social skills, self-assurance is most easily learned by on-the-job experience. A fear of the sea cannot be overcome without getting your feet wet. In the same way a shy person does not overcome their affliction by becoming a recluse, but by going out and meeting people and so enhancing their social skills. The greater our experience of any particular activity or situation – examinations, interviews, public speaking or child rearing – the less dread they hold for us.

  Someone who has never made a parachute descent from a plane is likely to view their first drop with considerable apprehension. But this dread can be lessened by appropriate training, in which basic falling skills are taught in a gymnasium and then rehearsed by taking practice jumps from an outside tower. Tests show that by using this schedule of gradual familiarisation, anxiety lessens as experience grows. In one trial trainee parachutists were asked to assess on a ten-point scale the amount of fear they experienced as they waited to jump from a thirty-foot practice tower. On their first jump the group reported feeling an average of six points of fear; a figure which dropped to three points by the time they were seasoned performers preparing for their seventh jump.

Anxiety can also be lessened by dummy exercises, such as fire drills, boardroom games, mock examinations and the simulated accidents used to train first-aid workers. Soldiers in peacetime are put through military exercises which prepare them for the manoeuvres of war and also give them the hardiness to withstand the psychological rigours of war. This was proved during the Second World War when it was found that nervous breakdowns in the British army were twice as common among wartime recruits as among trained, regular soldiers. One effect of this indoctrination process is that it improves our psychological coping skills. By repeated exposure we can attenuate our fear of war or parachute jumping, just as we can develop an immunity to tuberculosis by exposing our bodies to the tubercle bacillus (the micro-organism that causes the disease). Such training also strengthens our physiological defence mechanisms. This has been demonstrated by experiments in which laboratory animals have been subjected to bouts of intermittent stress, a procedure which causes an enlargement of their adrenal glands and therefore an increased capacity for producing corticosteroid stress hormones. As a result they are better prepared to cope with any future threats to their security.

How well do these training methods work in practice? Can confidence, 'hardiness' and self-assurance be taught, or are they innate qualities? The experience of the psychologists employed to study the plight of the Bell Telephone Company's highly stressed executives suggests that coping skills can indeed be acquired. They set up 'hardiness induction groups', designed to help restore the men's feeling of confidence and control. In one exercise they were encouraged to recall a recent stressful incident and then to think up three ways in which it might have turned out for the worse, and three ways in which it might not have had such a catastrophic outcome. In another lesson they were given advice on dealing with upheavals that could be neither avoided nor controlled, like the onset of serious illness or the death of a spouse. They were also taught a practical ego-boosting ploy, whereby they could compensate for failure in one area of their lives by immediately redirecting their attention to an alternative sphere of activity where they could demonstrate their competence and control. At the end of a course of eight lessons the group showed an increase in their hardiness ratings. They also reported fewer stress symptoms and significantly lower blood pressures than a control group of managers who did not receive the hardiness training.

In some cases timidity stems, not from lack of ability, but from fear of failure. We refuse to take risks because we do not want to lose face by coming a cropper in public. But there is considerable evidence to justify the motto of Britain's crack SAS Regiment: 'He who dares, wins'. During World War Two psychologist Dr Paul Torrence carried out a study of ace US pilots and discovered that one of their prime characteristics was an ability to take risks. This calculated daring improved their performance and, far from making them prone to accidents, actually added to their safety. As Dr Torrence concluded: 'Life itself is a risky business. If we spent half as much time learning how to take risks as we spend avoiding them, we wouldn't have so much to fear in life.' By taking risks and successfully overcoming challenges we increase in competence and grow in self-esteem.

- ## Act As If
  There are many times in life when we are liable to be overcome with doubts and fears. On these occasions, rather than sinking into a state of passive, non-productive anxiety, we should summon up our resolve and act as if we were confident, or behave as if we were sure. This is an effective and immediate way of increasing self-assurance, for as we think so we become. Theodore Roosevelt was a man of great moral courage and yet he admitted in his autobiography that as a boy he was nervous, awkward and timid. 'I had to train myself painfully and laboriously,' he wrote, to acquire the confidence and determination he showed in later life. He did this by following the technique advocated by a character

in one of Captain Marryat's novels who said that all men are frightened when they first go into battle, but can overcome their fear by acting as if they were brave and continuing to do so until pretence becomes reality. 'There were all kinds of things of which I was afraid at first, ranging from grizzly bears to "mean" horses and gun fighters,' Roosevelt confessed, 'but by acting as if I was not afraid I gradually ceased to be afraid.'

The power of this simple technique is awesome. This was revealed when a team of psychologists from Stanford University set up an experiment involving a simulated prison and a group of about two dozen mature, emotionally stable university students. At the flip of a coin the youngsters were assigned to the role of either prisoners or guards. From that point onward they were left to play their respective parts, acting as if they were either wardens or detainees. Within days their behaviour changed dramatically, so much so that the experiment had to be terminated after only six days. By this time many of the 'prisoners' were severely depressed, cowed and given to bouts of hysterical crying. Some of the guards had become tyrannical in the way they used their power, taking pleasure in cruelty and treating their charges like despicable animals. This remarkable transformation was summarised by Professor Philip Zimbardo, who led the project: 'In less than a week the experience of imprisonment undid (temporarily) a lifetime of learning; human values were suspended, self-concepts were challenged and the ugliest, most base, pathological side of human nature surfaced.' Such is the power of the 'acting as if' technique to modify human behaviour.

When psychologists meet, and have a few moments to spare, they often discuss the perennial problem of whether our bodily responses to emotion – muscle tension, increased sweating, sighing, respiration – are the causes or effects of our changing moods. Do we feel fear because our pulse races and our stomach churns, or do our hearts and stomachs become hyperactive because of the terror we feel? Whatever the rights and wrongs of this particular debate, there is indisputable evidence that we can exercise control over our emotions by modifying our bodily reactions. We feel less fear if we can calm our rate of breathing;

*experience less anger if we manage to keep our muscles relaxed; suffer less despondency if we can keep a smile on our face. It is no coincidence that when Stanislavski started out as a teacher of acting technique he advised his pupils to work their way into a role by conjuring up their memories of whatever emotion they needed to portray. But as he gained experience his ideas underwent a radical revision, and in later years he taught his students to construct their roles on physical actions rather than emotions. In this way they could create whatever mood they wished by employing the 'act as if' technique.*

Self-assurance can be built by techniques such as these. But no man functions in isolation. Our well-being depends as much on our intrinsic qualities as on our interpersonal relationships. This was well expressed over 2,000 years ago by Rabbi Hillel who said: 'If I am not for myself, who is for me; and being for my own self what am I?' This points to the fourth b-Attitude of Health – Conviviality – which will be discussed in the chapter which follows.

# Chapter Eleven:

# CONVIVIALITY
## *The Fourth b-Attitude of Health*

The human animal has two basic social needs, a need for an intimate, loving relationship with a parent or spouse and a need to feel part of a close, caring community. We are fundamentally group animals and our well-being is enhanced when we are in a convivial environment, in which we live in close communion, or *con-vivere*. Research has shown that when we are lonely we are more prone to accidents, mental illness, suicide and a wide range of diseases, such as cancer, tuberculosis and heart disease.

We need to love and be loved. For a while we can manage without affection, just as we can manage without food or water, but if the deprivation lasts too long we suffer sickness, unhappiness and even premature death. This was the conclusion reached by Dr James Lynch, who enumerated the medical consequences of loneliness in his book *The Broken Heart* in which he warned: 'We must either learn to live together or increase our chances of dying prematurely alone.'

Unfortunately the recent tendency has been to emphasise the demands of the individual over those of the group. This has been the age of the 'me' generation, a culture in which youngsters have been encouraged to undergo self-assertion training, to do their own thing and to form protest groups to challenge the habits and mores of society.

This cult of individualism is deeply enshrined in Western culture, which has invariably found rugged independence more praiseworthy than self-effacing group endeavour. Hence the folklore glorification of the eccentric genius, the lone ranger, the self-made businessman or the desert island castaway. This egocentricity is especially favoured in English-speaking countries, for English is the only major language which capitalises the letter 'I'. (In many other languages the personal pronoun 'i' is printed in the lower case, while the elevated status of capitalisation is reserved for the third person pronoun 'You'.)

A wholesome measure of independence and self-assurance is necessary for personal survival, but throughout our lives we cannot exist without the support and company of others. As the existentialists point out, you cannot have an 'I' without a 'you', any more than you can have a wife without a husband, or a teacher without pupils. But this social interdependence is far more than a remote philosophical concept, for it is also a fundamental human need. We need the co-operation of others to survive, whether we are living as primitive tribesmen in a tropical rain forest or as residents in a modern industrial city. From the earliest periods of recorded time our forebears welded themselves into social groups to clear the forests, build their homes, fight and hunt for food. We often look back on their way of life and view them as belligerent savages, whereas in fact a large part of their time was spent, not in conflict, but in peaceful collaboration. In order to survive, as Darwin stressed, they had to show amity as well as enmity.

It was this co-operative behaviour which enabled early man to survive, and which made him truly human, according to anthropologist Richard Leakey who traces twentieth-century man's development from the early hominids in *People of the Lake*. The early gatherer-hunters, Leakey emphasises, were not as aggressive and competitive as we generally assume. What separated them from their cousins the apes, was not their superior intelligence but their more highly developed generosity. 'Sharing,

161

not hunting or gathering as such, is what made us human,' he writes. 'We are human because our ancestors learned to share their food and skills in an honoured network of obligation.'

Some modern nations have managed to maintain this synergistic outlook. Youngsters in Thailand, for example, are taught to be caring and considerate. The prized goal for a cultured Thai is not to achieve material success at all costs, but to express *nam jai*, which literally means 'water of the heart', but is more accurately translated as the milk of human kindness. Even when they engage in martial arts, and join the Thai Sword-Fighting Institute, they are asked to sign an oath of allegiance to the group, swearing that they will never quarrel among themselves or harbour ill-feelings towards one another. How much more congenial life in the West would be if we agreed to sign a similar pact before joining sports clubs, churches, welfare groups, firms, charity committees and parent-teachers' associations.

We may pride ourselves on our independence but, whether we like it or not, we are *all* dependent on our kinsfolk for our survival. We wake up in the morning convinced of our total self-reliance, but before we set foot outside the house we will have demonstrated our dependence on an unseen army of nameless helpers. When we switch on the light we utilise the services of hundreds of workers in the electricity industry. When we brew a pot of early-morning tea we use tea leaves grown perhaps by farm labourers in India, and brought to us by a long chain of packers, wholesalers, distributors and retailers. The daily paper distributed to our door may have originated as Scandinavian woodpulp, before it took the shape given it by a team of journalists and printers. Even our morning bowl of muesli – with its mixture of nuts, raisins and oats – may be the product of several countries and thousands of pairs of hands.

We need other people's hands to feed us, others' arms to nurse us, others' lips to comfort us and others' bodies to defend us. 'No man is an Island, entire of itself,' said John Donne. And when we lose the protection of this complex social-support system our well-being and health invariably suffer. When Japanese men move to America to work they experience a massive increase in heart disease. At first this was attributed to the adoption of an unhealthy Western diet rich in animal fats, but it now seems more probable that it is due to cultural shock and the loss of the supportive network of family ties and friendship links. This theory gains additional support from the discovery that Swedish men are also far more prone to suffer coronary disease when they emigrate to the United States, even though there is no appreciable difference between the average Swedish and American diet.

Sickness rates rise whenever we are deprived of the companionship and support of our kith and kin. A British army study revealed that the neonatal death rate of babies born to the wives of soldiers transferred to the military garrison at Colchester was twice the national average. The wives were young, but apart from this the investigating doctors could advance only one possible explanation to explain the excess of infant deaths: the mother's isolation and lack of family support. In Scandinavia, a study of the life-styles and friendship links of over 17,000 Swedes revealed that even when allowance was made for differences in physical risk factors – age, smoking and physical inactivity – the subjects with few social contacts had a 40 per cent increased risk of suffering fatal cardiovascular disease. From this it would seem that a wealth of friends is a better agent of coronary care than a profusion of exercise.

Research reveals that companionship benefits a wide range of human activities. Students learn better when they study in groups than when they work on their own. Mothers with a high level of support from family and friends – described as 'psycho-social assets' – have three times less risk of suffering miscarriages, still births and other serious complications than those who lead a lonelier life. Even jet lag is less troublesome when we are in the company of friends than when we travel on our own.

At one time most people lived in tightly knit communities which provided them with a network of close relationships. They might have lacked material goods – washing machines, cars and television sets – but to compensate for this they had a wealth of 'psycho-social assets'. If at any time they needed sympathy, support or counselling they could easily obtain it from their neighbours, priest or families. This rarely applies today, for the populations of most industrial cities are now too large, too

163

transient and too heterogenic to permit the formation of close social ties. In these friendless circumstances people are often forced to *buy* sympathy and emotional support from professional counsellors. Or they can seek it from a doctor if they happen to be living in countries where medical services are provided as a free welfare benefit. This has greatly increased the work-load of general practitioners, who in addition to treating the sick are now expected to befriend the lonely, hearten the bereaved, reassure the anxious, comfort the dying and cheer the depressed. If they are not blessed with sympathetic neighbours, people will take their problems to their doctors. Some make surgery visits every week, to off-load their worries and get their ration of personal care. These 'fat file' cases take up a large proportion of a doctor's time, to the extent that 5 per cent of British patients are responsible for 20 per cent of all surgery consultations. The visits of these patients are often dreaded because of their constant demands, emotional dependency, never-ending litany of trivial complaints and poor response to treatment, which makes their doctors feel useless or at best inadequate. Studies of these regular attenders – often referred to in medical circles as 'heartsink' patients – show that they are rarely without symptoms of some kind. But the feature which most clearly distinguishes them from the rest of the population is their loneliness. They have 'less rich social lives' and a 'higher chance of being single or suffering from family dysfunction': this is how their plight has been summarised in a recent editorial in the *British Medical Journal*.

Zoo keepers and farmers recognise that animals are social beasts and need to be provided with suitable companionship if they are to thrive. Why are we so slow to recognise that exactly the same criterion applies to human welfare? The US authorities have introduced legislation to improve the well-being of dogs used by the country's scientific research institutes. This new code lays down that animals held for experimental purposes must be able to see and hear one another, or have 'positive physical contact with a human' for an hour a day. In addition the dogs must be released from their cages for half-an-hour a day for 'exercise and socialization'. This is a welcome attempt to improve the health of laboratory animals, but what of the health of animals caged in city apartment blocks? Since public health authorities recognise that exercise and socialisation are important for animals, why can they not accept that humans have a need for socialisation which is every bit as great as their need for aerobic exercise? Why spend so much money promoting jogging and calorie-reduced diets and yet ignore the fundamental human craving for companionship and social support?

Surveys suggest that loneliness is a significant cause of coronary disease. A detailed study revealed that the inhabitants of Framingham, a small, friendly Massachusetts town, had a mortality rate from coronary disease which was one-third the national average. This was attributed in large part to the fact that they were living in a well-integrated, stable society where divorce rates were well below the national average. Dr Stewart Wolf, Professor of Medicine at Temple University School of Medicine, Philadelphia, came to a similar conclusion when he studied the Pennsylvanian mining town of Roseto. Here he observed that the largely Italian population was in the habit of eating generous helpings of calorie-rich pasta and many other foods which cardiologists consider bad for the heart, and yet they had only a third as many heart attacks as neighbouring towns. What was the reason for their remarkable immunity? Professor Wolf had little doubt. 'The most striking feature of Roseto was its social structure,' he reported. 'Unlike most American towns Roseto is cohesive and mutually supportive, with strong family ties . . . The family was found to be the focus of life in Roseto. In addition few men over the age of 25 were unmarried.'

These same factors – social disruption, weak family bonds and emotional separateness – also appear to play a part in the development of cancer as demonstrated by researchers from the University of Rochester who found that a high proportion of cancer patients are rigid, aloof and undemonstrative. They withdraw from emotional contact with others and successfully manage to conceal their feelings so that they are neither openly affectionate nor overtly angry.

Dr Claus Bahnson of the Eastern Pennsylvania Psychiatric Institute made a very similar discovery when he compared a group of patients suffering from a number of other diseases and a similar bunch of healthy individuals. The outstanding difference between the three groups lay in their childhood relationships. The cancer subjects, he found, had a history of remote and unsatisfying relationships with their parents. 'People with this kind of background,' Dr Bahnson explained, 'are more vulnerable to loss in later life, because they have difficulty maintaining close relationships and lack outlet for intensified emotional charges.'

What is true of the social roots of cancer is equally true of the psycho-social origins of many other diseases. Various studies have shown that a breakdown of friendship ties – caused by death, separation, job changes or moving home – can provoke diseases such as hyperthyroidism, pulmonary tuberculosis, ulcerative colitis, Raynaud's disease and asthma. Another survey revealed that a key provocative factor in congestive heart failure was 'loss of security through rejection by some key figure upon whom the patient has been dependent'. We recognise that this sudden social deprivation can cause mental distress, but are often surprised to discover that it can also cause widespread damage to the body. This it does by provoking a wide range of biochemical changes.

Shift workers experience stress when they change their hours of duty. This is accompanied by an increase in their blood cholesterol levels, which places them at greater risk of suffering cardiovascular disease. But tests show that the increase in cholesterol levels is minimised when the men change shifts in company with their mates, rather than when they lose their comradeship and enter an alien working team. Similar considerations apply when men are made redundant, a stressful situation which threatens their security and self-esteem. These challenges bring about a rise in blood cholesterol levels, which once again are reduced if the men receive adequate social support from their families and network of friends.

Friendships are not one of life's optional extras, to be cultivated when we have time to spare. They are vital to our health and happiness. Friendships are a life-insurance policy, particularly for teenagers who are especially vulnerable to the effects of social isolation. This was disclosed by three Chicago researchers who engaged the help of twenty-five youngsters aged between thirteen and eighteen and equipped them with notebooks and mobile paging devices. For a week the youngsters undertook to write down whatever they were doing and feeling when the bleepers sounded. The results showed that they were happiest when they were playing games with their friends. This type of activity made them feel sociable, strong, active and free. The next most pleasurable pastime was talking with their friends, which took up more of their time than any other waking pursuit. This made them feel happy, friendly and sociable. Watching television made the second greatest demand on their time, often because they had nothing else to do. But this did not have the same cheering effect. In fact the researchers reported: 'When watching TV they tended not to feel happy or sad, friendly or hostile, strong or weak, lonely or sociable. Simply put, they did not feel.' When we are engaged in such mindless pursuits we tend to feel apathetic, a word derived from the Latin *a-pathos*, meaning without feeling. It is when we are in the company of friends that we normally experience depth of feeling. This was one of the maxims of Epicurus who said: 'Of all the means to ensure happiness throughout the whole of life, by far the most important is the acquisition of friends.'

We need friends to make us happy. Without them we all too easily become apathetic, morose or chronically depressed. This explains the close links between suicide and social alienation, first demonstrated by the French sociologist Emil Durkheim in his classic book *Suicide*, which was published in 1897. Durkheim analysed all the factors that could drive a person to end their lives – such as illness, bereavement and financial hardship – but concluded that the major determinant was what he described as 'social cohesion'. People who felt that they were part of a closely knit group were less likely to attempt suicide than those who were more isolated. In the same way Durkheim found that societies which encouraged strong communal ties and kinship links had a lower incidence of suicide than those which placed less emphasis on close interdependence. Recent experience has provided convincing support for Durkheim's views. The World Health Organisation has found that the more social supports a nation provides, the lower its suicide rate. This was clearly seen in

Britain during the 1960s and 1970s, when the introduction of a comprehensive social welfare system produced a 34 per cent drop in the country's suicide rate.

The therapeutic effect of social cohesion on the individual has been confirmed by several studies, most notably by that conducted over a nine-year period among seven thousand residents of Alameda County in California. This had the aim of identifying the factors – both physical and psycho-social – which provide protection from illness and premature death. In addition to assessing the importance of recognised risk factors such as smoking, lack of exercise and obesity, the researchers also investigated the relevance of four psycho-social factors: marital status, friendship networks, church affiliation and membership of community organisations. Each of these proved to be important determinants of health. So much so that unmarried individuals with few friends and no links with a church or outside community group had a death rate from all causes (including suicide) which was two to five times higher than those who had a well-developed network of friendships and acquaintances.

Both individuals and nations would benefit by the development of closer, happier community ties. Unfortunately our relationships with our neighbours today are less likely to be based on co-operation, than on competition or even outright conflict. This sad fact was demonstrated by a recent door-to-door survey around an estate in London which revealed that one resident in four was involved in long-standing disputes with their neighbours. This social disruption undermines personal health and happiness and also impedes national progress. All the great monuments to man's achievement were obtained through group endeavour. The Taj Mahal, for instance, is estimated to have occupied the labours of 22,000 men and women for a period of twenty-two years. Nowadays there may no longer be a demand for us to collaborate to build national shrines, but we still need to labour together to construct an environment which is safe, clean, healthy and aesthetically pleasing. We can safeguard our homes from burglars by taking part in Neighbourhood Watch schemes. We can foster the education of our children by becoming active members of a Parent Teachers' Association. We can help protect our environment by joining preservation societies. Even the risk of fires would be reduced if we took our responsibilities as citizens more seriously, according to a study which revealed that during a single year the city of Boston suffered a spate of 200 fires which burned out of control. During the same year Zurich, a town of almost identical size, experienced only eight unrestrainable fires, an incredible difference which, since the firefighters of the two towns had equally sophisticated equipment and training, was attributed to the greater assistance provided by the Swiss people in reporting the fires and helping to bring them under immediate control. As the US Health Education Foundation commented, when reporting the study: 'The Swiss have more experience than we do at living closely together in cities. They share a homogeneity of culture and values that we Americans lack.'

It would be both a national and personal tragedy if, in our march to assert our freedom and individual autonomy, we lost the ability and willingness to take part in communal activities. This is where Western society must change, to provide greater encouragement for group endeavour and slightly less tolerance and reward for uncaring individualism. In this respect we have much to learn from the members of most 'primitive' races, whose primary responsibility is to the tribe rather than to the individual. The Hopi Indians of Arizona, for example, spent their entire day in co-operative group activities – hunting, farming, herding cattle, collecting fuel and weaving cloth. For them it was no shame to be poor. Their greatest social crime was to opt out of activities and ceremonies which benefited the community. At school they would become embarrassed if they were singled out for individual praise, and when they played games they did so purely for fun rather than for the glory of winning. So much so that children would refuse to keep score when they played baseball, and would finish the game without any conception of which side had won or lost.

This spirit of friendly, non-antagonistic collaboration is rarely encountered in the West today, except in rare circumstances. Many ex-servicemen still experience a nostalgic longing for the comradeship they experienced during the war. Although their lives as front-line troops were tough and dangerous, they had the recompense of being part of a closely knit team. Army psychiatrists claim that this intimate group relationship played a vital role in maintaining morale and preserving the mental health of combat troops. This was one of the major medical discoveries of the war, according to the Office of the US Surgeon General, which published a retrospective survey of the incidence of psychiatric illness during the war. The report said: 'Perhaps the most significant contribution of World War II military psychiatry was the recognition of the sustaining influence of the small combat group or particular members thereof, variously termed "group identification", "group cohesiveness", "the buddy system" and "leadership". This was also operative in non-combat situations. Repeated observations indicated that the absence or inadequacy of such sustaining influences or their disruption during combat was mainly responsible for psychiatric breakdown in battle.'

In time of war it is easy to see the necessity for cohesive group behaviour. In peacetime the value of concerted, communal endeavour is equally great, but far less apparent. The main dangers to society today come not from without, but from within. Our cities are not threatened by invading armies, but by the disruptive influences of crime, environmental pollution, racial intolerance, loneliness, illiteracy, social divisiveness, family disruption, unhappiness, greed, drug abuse and unemployment. These are social problems which diminish the quality of our individual lives; yet they cannot be solved by individuals working on their own. Utopian societies arise only when individuals agree to subjugate their individual wants and needs so that they can work together for the common good. This is the basis of *all* civilised communities, for the definition of a society in *Webster's Dictionary* is 'an enduring and co-operating social group whose members have developed organised patterns of relationships through interaction with one another'.

In the creation of this communal paradise we have much to learn from the animal kingdom and its example of 'reciprocal altruism'. Animals will resort to violence if this is necessary to defend their lives or territorial rights. But the majority of animals also have an instinct to act in consort to support their fellows.

These twin drives appear different on the surface but actually serve an identical purpose – the survival of the species. For this reason a mother will sacrifice her life to save her child. A drone bee will struggle to win the race to copulate with his queen, even though he is destined to expire once his brief moment of glory is over. Similarly, the phagocyte cells in our bodies, which will fight valiantly to engulf invading germs even though they are doomed to perish in the attempt. All die in the cause of corporate survival.

It is easy for us to accept 'reciprocal altruism' as merely an abstract concept. During times of war some may even make the noble sacrifice and lay down their lives for their friends. But in times of prosperity and peace it is far easier to let self-interest take precedence over group loyalty. 'United we stand, divided we fall' may be the rallying call during periods of national crisis. But in periods of material prosperity the battle cry becomes 'Every man for himself'. And yet if we are to build a happy, peaceful, caring society we must achieve a union between our twin survival drives – the instinct of self-preservation and the innate drive to take part in preserving the interest of the herd. This may seem an idealistic notion, but to many scientists it represents the only hope for man's survival. Professor Hans Selye came to this conclusion after spending a lifetime studying the effects of stress on human biochemistry. He favoured the adoption of a philosophy of 'altruistic egoism'. To avoid communal strife and achieve personal health and happiness, he said, we should order our lives in such a way that we earn the love and gratitude of those around us. 'I know of no other philosophy which necessarily transforms all our egotistic impulses into altruism without curtailing any of their self-protecting values.'

Unfortunately, instead of drawing closer together, the communities of the Western world seem to be growing further apart. Loneliness is rife in the big cities. Alienation is now cited as one of the major causes of psychiatric illness. When *Woman's Realm* carried out a survey of its readers it discovered 'a frighteningly high incidence of loneliness'. Nearly a quarter of the sample, both single and married, complained of a dearth of companionship, which suggests that there may be seven million lonely women in Britain alone. How has this alienation arisen? Many contributory causes have been cited, including increased social mobility, repeated job and home transfers, smaller, inward-looking family units, the growth of megalithic industrial cities and the decline in group activities such as church-going and community singing and dancing. All of these factors probably play their part.

A generation ago the majority of families lived out their lives within a single village community; now the average American moves house approximately fourteen times. This nomadic existence gives rise to separation stress, particularly among the young and elderly, because it inevitably results in a repeated severance of friendship ties. The loss of this network of social support causes an increased susceptibility to illness and even an increased risk of death. This was demonstrated when the medical records were examined of a hundred British families settling into a new housing estate. To begin with they made an above-average number of visits to their doctors; then gradually their excessively high consultation rate fell as they settled into the unfamiliar environment and made new friends. Some people appear to be more prone than others to suffer separation anxiety. This applies particularly to the elderly, who find it difficult to adapt to dramatic changes in their environment and social setting. Health workers in Chicago discovered this when they were forced to close a home for incurables and relocate the patients elsewhere. Divorced from the surroundings, inmates and helpers they knew so well, the invalids suffered a marked decline in health. Within three months a sixth of them had died, a mortality rate which was five times above the national average for people of their age and physical condition.

Loneliness arises from moving home, and particularly from migrating into the large, amorphous industrial cities. We, just as much as wolves and eagles, are territorial animals. We like to have the company and support of other members of our species, but we also like to preserve our privacy and maintain our patch of personal territory. If this is invaded, as it often is in densely populated urban districts, we suffer stress. The harmful effects of this social overcrowding, and also of loneliness, have been clearly demonstrated in animal experiments. In one test groups of mice susceptible to mammary cancer were housed in conditions of varying social density. Some were assigned to open cages in groups of fifty, a community size which they seemed to tolerate well. Others were put in the same-sized cages after they had been divided into ten separate compartments – like apartments in a high-rise block of flats – so that there were five mice in each small cubicle. Still more were placed in solitary confinement in small glass jars. At the end of the test it was found that the rate of cancer development was nearly twice as high in the mice who had been held in the compartment homes as in those who had been allowed a more free-ranging, sociable existence. But the greatest risk was shown by the lonely mice who developed more cancers than either of the other groups.

There is no doubt that compartment-block living is not ideal for laboratory mice, nor for urban man. Although there appears to be no consensus of opinion about the ideal density of human housing, there are some clear indications regarding the optimum size of towns. In medieval times many European towns were limited in size because it was felt necessary for the inhabitants to remain within earshot of the bells of the parish church, which called them to worship and also gave them notice of births, deaths, weddings and states of emergency. This requirement limited the size of towns to perhaps a thousand homes. Similar constraints applied in the Middle East, where villagers needed to be within hearing distance of the mosque so that they could all hear the voice of the muezzin calling them to prayer. These communities would have housed 2,000 to 5,000 people, a population size which would have permitted a wide range of social contacts and a keen sense of belonging. This is impossible within a modern industrial city where it is difficult to feel part of a community, although even in these vast conurbations people try to imagine that their home and its immediate environs constitute a neighbourhood of a sort. This was demonstrated when a group of Cambridge housewives were given an area map and asked to draw a circle around what they thought to be *their* neighbourhood. Three-quarters of the sample delineated an area which averaged 100 acres. If the population density of the region was forty people to the acre, a common figure for residential areas with detached housing, this would give a neighbourhood grouping of 4,000 people. Opinion polls in America suggest that this is a congenial size for town communities, for when questioned people living in towns with fewer than 2,500 inhabitants express more dissatisfaction with their lives than those living in communities with 2,500 to 5,000 residents. People living in cities with populations exceeding a million are less satisfied still, but even they report a higher level of contentment than those living in sparsely populated rural districts. From this it would seem that, like the laboratory mice, we are happier when we are part of a conveniently sized community, than when we are overcrowded or, worse still, excessively isolated.

The introduction of modern technology has also added to our loneliness. Women living a century ago in a British market town had ample opportunity for social contact. Each morning, in company with their neighbours, they drew water from a communal pump or well. Later in the day they did their shopping in the village store, which gave them a further chance to gossip. Several times a week they did the family laundry, often at a communal washing point. Nowadays every one of these opportunities for social intercourse has disappeared. Water is piped directly to the house, so there is no need to visit the village well. Shopping is done, not once a day but possibly once a fortnight, at a vast emporium where it is quite possible to enter and leave the store without exchanging a word with a single person. And nowadays there is generally no chance to natter over the garden fence while the washing is being hung out to dry, for modern washing-machines and spin-driers make it possible to launder clothes indoors. In the same way most of our news of community events, scandals and tragedies is supplied by local radio and newspapers rather than by village gossip.

Even our leisure time today tends to be spent in isolation. Instead of becoming part of an intimate church congregation on a Sunday many prefer to worship in solitude by listening at home to broadcast religious services. Instead of attending public concerts we listen in privacy to recorded music. Instead of *living* an intimate communal life, with all its inevitable emotional traumas and personality clashes, the contemporary urbanite watches life from afar, by becoming a voyeur of TV soap operas. Even when we leave our domestic hermitages we can do so now in total seclusion, for the modern motor car makes it possible to travel in social quarantine, rather than mix with others in public buses, trains and stagecoaches. Although our social situation has changed dramatically, our need for companionship remains as urgent as ever. Our forebears secured their necessary ration of conviviality as an automatic by-product of their involvement in small-scale community life. Today, particularly if we live in large conurbations, we can no longer rely on being the inevitable recipients of this vital, social nutrient. Millions of people throughout the Western world are at risk of suffering sickness, depression and even premature death through social deprivation. We recognise that sickness can result from a lack of vitamins or dearth of exercise; what we must also recognise is that illness can also stem from a deficiency of social contacts.

Ideally we start our social life by establishing an intimate relationship with our parents, and forging an especially close link with our mothers. This makes an enormous difference to our well-being and also to our mental development, as Dr Rene Spitz of New York discovered when he made a study of two groups of children who were identical in all respects except that one set was cared for by their mothers and the other from the age of three months onwards by nursery nurses who were too busy to give the infants the individual care and attention they needed. At the start of the study each child was given a Development Quotient (DQ), a measurement which was based on their social relations, intelligence, memory, perception and manipulative skills. The results indicated that the children cared for by their mothers showed a slight increase in their DQ during the first two years of the study, whereas the youngsters brought up in the institution suffered a dramatic fall from a DQ of 124 initially, to 72 at the end of the first year and as little as 45 after two years. During the period of the study the institutionalised children were backward in learning to speak, walk and feed themselves, and 37 per cent of them died during the first five years of their lives, a fate not suffered by any of the children who had the benefit of their mothers' love and care.

As we mature we cease to be dependent on our mothers, but we still have the need for an intimate loving relationship. To satisfy this longing we normally enter into a number of close pair bondings soon after we enter our teens and eventually generally settle down in marriage. This gives us a second chance at establishing an intimate personal relationship, for even if we have been orphaned at an early age, or had a traumatic relationship with our mothers, we can through the experience of marriage learn to be part of a close, caring partnership. The establishment of this intimate relationship is a major aid to health, for statistics reveal that the death rates of single people are higher than for those who are married. They also pay more frequent visits to their doctors and are more likely to spend time in hospital. Bachelors even earn less than married men, are twice as likely to have a prison sentence, commit suicide more often and die at an earlier age. When a married man related these figures to one of his single friends the bachelor replied: 'So now I know what to do. If I want a long, lingering death I must get married.'

But the married state, if it is to be life enhancing, must be reasonably harmonious. This was demonstrated by Dr J. H. Medalie who followed the lives of 10,000 Israeli males who at their initial examination were shown to be free of detectable heart disease. In the years which followed it was found that the men who developed heart disease were much more likely to have reported dissatisfaction with their married lives. Their main complaint was not that their wives did not understand them, but that they did not give them adequate emotional support.

The need to be loved was appreciated by doctors in the past, but is often overlooked by physicians today. Paracelsus claimed that love was one of the four pillars of medicine. Erasistratus, a physician who lived three centuries before the birth of Christ, also understood the healing power of love. He was called to treat a young prince who was losing weight and would not eat. The cause of his malaise was not apparent, until Erasistratus noticed that his pulse rate quickened whenever one of his father's young and beautiful wives appeared. Realising that his patient was probably suffering from unrequited love rather than from an obscure wasting disease, the astute physician persuaded the king to let his son marry the object of his desire. Immediately the prince recovered.

Many lonely or lovelorn people today visit their doctors with similar strange complaints; but they do not want pills, their basic need is for companionship and affection. This was recognised by psychoanalyst Erich Fromm, who in his book *The Art of Loving* said: 'The deepest need of man is the need to overcome separateness, to leave the prison of his aloneness.' The fundamental question, says Fromm, 'is how to overcome separateness, how to achieve union, how to transcend one's own individual life and find at-one-ment'.

These social goals can be met in the following ways:

● **Give To Get**
*Many people are so shy, or so afraid of suffering an emotional rebuff, that they are reluctant to be the first one to offer the hand of friendship. This is a sure recipe for loneliness. Far better to follow the counsel of St John of the Cross who advised: 'Where you do not find love, put love and you will find love.' In many ways the offering of affection is a conditioned response. If our behaviour to outsiders causes them unhappiness or pain they will avoid us, but if social contact with us is rewarding they will cultivate our friendship. This tendency is clearly seen in the training of household pets. If we treat a dog badly it will reject us, or turn surly and snap at our heels; if we treat it with care and affection it will become a loving and devoted companion. The same applies to the human animal. Everyone we meet has a need for love and affection. Our capacity for making warm relation-ships depends on our ability to meet this fundamental need. We cannot expect to reap a rich harvest of love unless we first broadcast the seeds of caring and compassion. 'The means to gain happiness,' wrote Leo Tolstoy, 'is to throw out for oneself like a spider in all directions an adhesive web of love, and to catch*

*in it all that comes.' The art of cultivating loving friendships lies in being a go-giver rather than a go-getter.*

- ## Love Yourself
  *Before we can love others, naturally and spontaneously, we must first learn to love ourselves. This truth is recognised by the followers of Buddha, who when they are meditating to enhance their love for their fellow men will always begin by concentrating their thoughts on their love for themselves. The same principle is encapsulated in Christian thought and teaching. When Jesus said: 'Love thy neighbour as thyself', he meant just that: that we should love our neighbours – not more nor less – but in the same way and to the same extent that we love ourselves. We will not be at ease in the company of others unless we are at peace with ourselves; and we will not be free to love others if we are unable to love ourselves.*

- ## Love Your Enemies
  *Most people find it reasonably easy to love their neighbours – providing the neighbours are convivial, law-abiding, considerate, friendly and quiet. The difficulty is to love one's enemies. At first sight this oft-repeated injunction may seem to present an impossible task. Our natural reaction is to feel anger, bitterness and resentment when we are subjected to abuse. Why should we love slanderers and cheats? Why should we turn the other cheek when people take advantage of us? Forgiveness in these instances is often advocated for abstruse theological reasons, but it is far more easily defended on physiological grounds. What happens if we do not forgive our enemies? If we harbour hatred we perpetuate stress responses within our bodies – muscular tension, raised blood pressure, increased secretion of gastric acids – which are harmful to our long-term health. Hatred is an indulgence we cannot afford, not because it is unkind to our enemies but because it is harmful to ourselves. Doctors have studied the gastric function of human volunteers, and have found that if they are made angry by accusations of being slow,*

*inefficient or greedy, the linings of their stomachs become red and swollen and bathed with increased quantities of acid juice. These conditions favour the production of gastric ulcers, proving that we can indeed be 'eaten up' with anger. Others when they are enraged become victims of tension headaches or high blood pressure.*

*One simple way of checking these self-destructive responses is to make an effort to depersonalise situations which tend to provoke our anger or resentment. When people commit an error we ought to criticise the fault, while remembering that there is still much to praise in the person. Even blackmailers and thieves are human beings like ourselves, with attributes as well as failings. In our dealings with them we will suffer less if we follow the principle of 'Loving the sinner, but hating the sin'. Even if we cannot bring ourselves to love our enemies, we should at least learn to feel goodwill towards them for that alone will be sufficient to check the damaging biological accompaniments of bitterness and hate.*

## • Cultivate Friendships

*Nothing good is achieved without effort, a maxim which applies to friendships as well as book learning, artistry and business success. In the course of an average day we may come into contact with a hundred people. If we bothered to make their acquaintance, we might find that we could make a close friend of only one of these passing encounters. From this it follows that if we want to build up a wide circle of intimate friends we need to be constantly ready to break the ice with strangers. Some people adopt the goal of trying to talk to someone fresh every day. This is a sensible policy, for these chance encounters are the warp and weft of communal living and could be the start of an enduring friendship.*

## • Breaking the Ice

*The biggest barriers to socialisation are almost certainly shyness and embarrassment. We refrain from introducing ourselves to strangers because we fear we may make fools of ourselves, we may not know what to say or they may not welcome our attentions. To overcome these obstacles the small Black Forest town of Enzklosterle issues coloured badges to holidaymakers seeking companionship. Those who want a hiking partner sport a green badge. Other coloured 'signal pins' indicate that the wearer is trying to locate fellow chess or bridge players. And red simply means, 'I want someone to talk to'. This arrangement has proved extremely successful and since its introduction the town authorities have distributed well over 10,000 pins.*

*Friendship schemes like this are popular, as are the lonely hearts columns of magazines, because many otherwise mature adults are reluctant to make their own social introductions. This reticence often stems from a fear of being misunderstood, slighted or rebuffed by strangers. Many people lead friendless lives, not because they are unattractive but because they would rather experience the long-term pangs of loneliness than suffer the occasional pains of humiliation and rejection. But if we are realistic, we must assume that some of our social overtures will be ignored, while others will lead to relationships which are both flimsy and fleeting. Like the sower in the New Testament parable, we must distribute our seeds of friendship liberally, knowing full well that some will fall on stony ground where they will not take root, while others will land on impoverished earth where they will flourish for a brief while and then wither away. But a few will fall on fertile soil where they will flourish and bear fruit a hundred-fold. Since we do not know in advance which of our seeds is destined to germinate in this way we have no alternative but to be generous in the way we broadcast our friendship. Certainly we can be sure that we will never reap lasting friendships if we are too fearful or too lazy to sow the initial seeds of amity.*

### • Keep Your Friendships in Repair

*Some years ago I was rash enough to become the publisher of a small, private circulation magazine. By the end of my first year in business I had made a succession of mistakes, the most* disastrous of which was to assume that every one of my current supporters would renew their subscriptions at the turn of the year. Magazine readers, I quickly discovered, are exceedingly fickle creatures, which is why publishers of successful magazines like Time and the Reader's Digest are always striving to find new subscribers to replace the ones they lose. Now I know that friends are far more loyal than magazine readers, but even they cannot be considered a permanence, for old school comrades die, working colleagues retire and neighbours move to another district. Because of this, if we want to avoid a lonely old age, we must be constantly engaged in reviving old friendships and forging new relationships.

People selling life insurance policies employ a technique known as 'networking'. This involves the use of the chain mail principle, whereby every friend and acquaintance acts as the source of another six or more 'prospects'. In this way a wide circle of valuable contacts can be acquired in a very brief time. When this technique is applied to the development of a wide network of friends it conveys considerable psycho-social benefits, as was discovered when a survey was made of all conscripts joining the Swedish army during the year 1969–70. The men were required to complete a detailed questionnaire, which included a declaration of their existing friendship links. Thirteen years later a follow-up study was made to see how the group of over 50,000 men had fared. One tragic finding was that nearly five in every 1,000 of the original conscripts had experienced such despair in the intervening years that they had taken their own lives. But this fatal decision was not taken at random. Analysis showed that the incidence of suicide was significantly less than average among the men who had the support of three or more friends. Among those who reported having only a single friend, the rate was nearly twice the group mean. But the highest rate of self-destruction was encountered among the men who had originally admitted to being totally friendless. They experienced a suicide rate which was nearly four times higher than the average for the group.

Many of us complain that we are too busy to keep our

friendship ties intact. But if we can find time to play golf, tennis and squash to improve our physical fitness, could we not find similar time to maintain our equally vital psycho-social health? This can only be done by means of regular personal contact, through meetings, social gatherings, dinners, parties, family get-togethers, phone calls and letters. In the frenzy of contemporary life we often fail to maintain these vital social links. This is particularly true of the forgotten art of letter writing. Many eminent figures of the past led lives which were every bit as active as ours, and yet they managed to maintain a voluminous correspondence. Charles Dickens was a perfect example. He had an enormous appetite for work and during a typical period of his life was reported as writing a novel a year, travelling extensively, lecturing, producing amateur theatricals for his friends, editing the magazine Household Words and running a home for fallen women. But he still found time to write an average of 100 letters a day! George Bernard Shaw, another inveterate correspondent, is credited with having written 250,000 letters during his lifetime. Some of these missives went to the famous figures of the day, like Churchill, Nehru, H. G. Wells, Paul Robeson and W. B. Yeats. Others were sent to total strangers who sought his help, like the Texan cowboy who asked his views on the ethics of cattle branding and the mother who feared that a maternity hospital had handed her the wrong child. Think how much richer our lives would be if the morning post brought us letters of goodwill from our friends instead of the usual bag of circulars, bills and charity demands.

'Fellowship is Life' was the dictum of William Morris, the Victorian poet and craftsman. But friendships do not happen, they have to be forged and fostered. Once created they play a major role in maintaining not only our health but also our happiness. This was recognised centuries ago by Ailred the Northumbrian who wrote: 'There is nothing in the world more valuable than friendship. Those men who banish friendship from their lives remove as it were the sun from the earth, because of all God's gifts to man, it is the most beautiful and the most pleasing.'

- **Show Kindness and Caring**

  *The test of true friendship lies in the extent to which we share our partners' feelings, moods, interests, disappointments, triumphs, griefs and pains. If we are to have a meaningful relationship we must be in sympathy with one another, a Greek word which means sym-pathos or 'shared feeling'. Strangely enough this emotional reciprocity is not difficult to foster, for it is an inherent human attribute. Providing we 'tune in' to their unspoken messages we can pick up other people's moods as easily as we can monitor a radio broadcast.*

  *One of the most remarkable demonstrations of this hidden power was provided at Harvard University Medical School, where a psychiatric team led by Dr Milton Greenblatt monitored the heart rates of patients and psychiatrists taking part in forty-four routine psychotherapy sessions. Visually it was clear that during the treatment sessions the doctors shared their patients' moods, for their speech patterns, facial expressions and bodily movements changed in concert, as they discussed matters which provoked anger, sadness or despondency. But a far more impressive indication of their emotional synergy was provided by the polygraph tracings which showed that their heart rates tended to rise and fall in unison. Moreover it was discovered when the sessions were over that the closeness of these movements was exactly mirrored by the closeness of their rapport. At times when the psychiatrists felt particularly close to their patients their heart rate patterns achieved the closest match; but when their rapport was broken by other preoccupations or outside distractions the congruence was less defined. From this it is clear that it is no exaggeration to talk, as poets do, of 'two hearts beating as one'.*

  *In the same way there is no doubt that we can feel other people's pain, as sensitive husbands sometimes do when their wives give birth. (In some of the more remote parts of South America men still observe the old custom of couvade, in which they take to their beds and writhe and moan while their wives are in labour.)*

  *To utilise and develop the power of empathy it is merely necessary to put yourself in other people's shoes and try to* imagine how they think and feel. This is the way to gain friends and also to become a successful conversationalist. Most people sought the company of Dr Johnson, not because he was a physically attractive man but because he was a fascinating talker. This skill stemmed from the fact that he always appeared more interested in other people than in himself. One of his biographers commented on his 'readiness to throw himself into the interests of other people' and added: 'He was a man who would have enjoyed discussing the making of spectacles with a spectacle maker, law with a lawyer, pigs with a pig breeder, diseases with a doctor, or ships with a ship-builder.'

The kindness which Dr Johnson dispensed is a universal language which the deaf can hear and the dumb can speak. When we experience anger and hatred we and we alone suffer; but when we distribute kindness and love both we and the recipients are the immediate beneficiaries. This was suggested by an unconfirmed study carried out at Harvard University in which students showed an improvement in their immune response after merely watching a film of Mother Teresa offering comfort and help to the sick and dying slum dwellers in Calcutta. By helping others, we help ourselves.

## • Eliminate the Negative

By showing empathy we strengthen the bonds of friendship, but we must never forget that the channels of emotional communication by which we forge friendships can also be used to transmit psychic poisons. When we share positive feelings with our friends – joy, compassion, understanding, caring and pride in our mutual achievements – our lives are enriched. But when we trade negative emotions – anger, bitterness, doubt and fear – our lives will be impoverished. This is why our choice of friends is so vitally important. If we want to be happy and healthy we should spend as much time as we can with happy, positive people. In the same way if we want to avoid sickness and despondency we should spend as little time as possible with morbid people who constantly display a negative attitude to life. By our friends we will be known and like our friends we will become.

*We often take pride in our independence, but few of us realise the profound extent to which we are conditioned by the moods of those around us. This was shown in an experiment in which a group of university students was given an injection of adrenalin, which was claimed to be part of an investigation in 'visual perception'. Afterwards they were given a variety of spurious suggestions concerning the likely effects of the injection and then asked to sit in an outside waiting room where their behaviour was closely observed. Here they came into contact with another student who was said to be taking part in the same experiment, but who was actually a confederate of the researchers engaged to simulate a variety of moods. The results showed that the response of the test subjects was not so much influenced by the injections they received, or by the reactions they had been encouraged to expect, as by the behaviour of the stool pigeons with whom they shared the room. When these temporary companions gave the impression of being angry, they too felt angry. When the stooges went through the motions of being euphoric, they too experienced feelings of euphoria. Obviously we are not only what we think and feel, but equally well what those about us think and feel.*

## ● Observe the Golden Rule

*In our relationships with other people we need to monitor not only our feelings but also our actions. Here our conduct should be guided by the simple principle reiterated in remarkably similar terms in the holy scriptures of all the world's major religions:*

Brahminism: *This is the sum of duty: Do naught unto others which would cause pain if done to you.* Mahabharata 5: 1517

Buddhism: *Hurt not others in ways that you yourself would find hurtful.* Udanavarga 5:18

Christianity: *All things whatsoever ye would that men should do to you, do ye even so to them.* Matthew 7:12

Confucianism: *Do unto others what you would have them do unto you.* Analaects 15:23

185

*Islam: No one of you is a believer until he desires for his brother that which he desires for himself. Sunan*

*Judaism: What is hateful to you, do not to your fellow man. That is the entire Law; all the rest is commentary. Talmud, Shabbat 31a*

*Taoism: Regard your neighbour's gain as your own gain, and your neighbour's loss as your own loss. T'ai-Shang Kan-Ying P'ien*

*The observance of this widely recognised Golden Rule would do more to foster peace among the people of this world than any conceivable act of international statesmanship or legislation. If we care for the interests of our friends as keenly as we fight to promote our own self-interest, there would be far fewer neighbourhood feuds and far less loneliness and alienation within our communities. Our individual health would also prosper since we would be surrounded by affection and care rather than by indifference and aggression.*

- ## Cultivate the Social Graces
  *If we are to live in close communion with other people we need to observe the etiquettes and behavioural laws which have been developed over the years to oil the wheels of social intercourse. These niceties appear to be falling into neglect in the Western world but are still observed by the majority of 'savage' tribes who, while they can be belligerent when the occasion demands, are normally polite, considerate, friendly and gentle. These primitive people can also be exceedingly generous and in some cases have made an art form of philanthropy. This is particularly true of the Eskimos who hold spectacular present-giving parties – known as potlach ceremonies – which in their lavishness and scale far exceed our annual distribution of Christmas gifts. A similar degree of munificence is shown by the Blackfoot Indians during their 'giveaway' Sun Dance ceremonies. When Abraham Maslow, the American psychologist, visited one of these spectacular events he saw a chieftain making a heap of his entire possessions, including blankets and crates of Pepsi-Cola, which he then gave away to the tribe's widows, orphans, sick and blind. 'At the*

end of the Sun Dance Ceremony,' said Maslow, 'he was stripped of all his possessions, owning nothing but the clothes he stood in.' Our communal lives would be enriched if we ourselves performed modest potlach rites – the distribution of 'thank you' cards, 'get-well' messages, bunches of flowers and unexpected gifts – to demonstrate our empathy, caring and friendship.

- ## Praise Often, Condemn Rarely
  It is always easier to criticise someone's shortcomings than to extol their virtues. Yet behavioural psychologists have shown that the carrot of praise is a far more effective motivator of human behaviour than the stick of disapproval – and a much more satisfactory way of preserving human friendships. People who go through life handing out bouquets rather than brickbats – a smile, a pat on the back and the occasional word of encouragement – do more to create harmony and lower tension levels than a wagonload of tranquillisers.

  Often it is difficult to resist the temptation to find fault with other people's behaviour. This destructive behaviour is often the expression of a psychological defence mechanism known as projection, the blame-transmitting ploy by which we attribute to others the faults we are unwilling to acknowledge in ourselves. One way of overcoming this nit-picking tendency is to make a rule of refraining from criticising other people's behaviour until we are fully acquainted with their circumstances. With better understanding of their predicament and a clearer appreciation of their motives we will probably find less cause for condemnation. For, in the words of the old French adage: 'Tout savoir, c'est tout pardonner' (To know all is to forgive all).

  Here again we have much to learn from the older cultures, many of which show great tolerance and understanding of the peccadillos of others, a forbearance which is delightfully expressed in the Red Indian prayer: 'Grant that I may not criticise my neighbours until I have walked a mile in their moccasins.'

  Tact, courtesy, gentleness, understanding, forgiveness and generosity are the behavioural traits which improve human relationships, stimulate friendships and thereby enhance our

187

neurohormonal health. *These qualities also enable groups of disparate individuals to work together as a cohesive and effective team, which means that by exercising these social skills we will ensure not only our own survival but also that of the communities in which we live and work.*

- ## Take Part in Small-group Activities
  *Over the millennia the human animal has become adapted to operating in small working groups of between ten to twelve people and to living in communities with a population of 3,000 to 5,000 individuals. One of our contemporary dilemmas is that we are often expected to work in multinational corporations with thousands of employees and live in a vast metropolis with several million inhabitants. Within these megatribes we find it very difficult to establish any sense of belonging, identity or community of purpose. One way of overcoming this sense of alienation is to make a conscious effort to join bands of like-minded individuals – church congregations, sports clubs, choirs, hobby societies, drama groups or local political parties. In this way we can rediscover a sense of community, companionship, group identity and shared purpose.*

  *The French Republic took as its motto the battle cry: Liberté! Egalité! Fraternité! We today are ready to fight for our liberty, and are struggling to impose a spurious equality. What we need to pursue now with equal zeal is a genuine spirit of fraternity.*

- ## Keep In Touch
  *Touch is one of the most important mediums of non-verbal communication. By a gentle caress we express affection; with a firm handshake we offer friendship; through a pat on the back we convey approval; with a comforting arm we offer sympathy and support. The importance of this ancient method of communication is recognised in our everyday speech, when we speak of 'keeping in touch' with our friends, 'rubbing' our neighbours up the wrong way, and 'handling' our enemies with care.*

  *Yet we seem to be losing the art of physical intimacy, a decline* which is weakening the bonding of groups and straining marital relationships. Some while ago Relate, the Marriage Guidance Council, published a document which expressed the view that the rising divorce rate in Britain was largely due to a lack of physical contact within the English family. According to the Council, the English 'need to touch, stroke and comfort one another more often'. The same is true of most other Western nations, which seem to place a puritanical taboo on all forms of intimate physical contact other than the purely formal hand-shake. The dangers of this aloofness were demonstrated by an investigation carried out at a psychiatric clinic at Nashville, Tennessee. This revealed that many depressed people yearn above all else for the comfort of being held, cuddled, fondled and stroked. Over half the depressed women interviewed admitted that they engaged in sexual intercourse simply as a means of gaining physical intimacy. Their basic need was not for sex but for close human contact.

Experiments show that this manipulative contact is vital for the health and development of animals. Tests performed at the Wistar Institute of Anatomy, Philadelphia, have shown that the regular handling of laboratory animals makes them more relaxed, less irritable and more resistant to stress. If they are subjected to experimental operations, regularly handled animals survive while those denied physical contact die. Other studies have shown that the early handling of animals stimulates their rate of growth, increases their level of activity and enhances their resistance to infection.

Human contact – touching, fondling and petting – also has a beneficial effect on the function of the heart. This was shown at the Johns Hopkins University School of Medicine when experiments were carried out to establish conditioned reflexes in dogs. It was discovered that when the animals were alone in their cages their hearts pounded at an unusually rapid rate of 120–160 beats per minute. This hectic pace lessened as soon as one of the researchers entered the room to provide them with a little company, which produced a slowing of 20–30 beats a minute. A still greater fall occurred when the dogs were fondled, which reduced their stress and slowed their hearts to a rate of only 40–

*60 beats per minute, or less than a third of their initial pace. The remarkable sedative effect of fondling was highlighted later on in the Johns Hopkins' experiments when the dogs were subjected to unexpected electric shocks applied to their forelimbs. Not surprisingly, the sudden pain made them withdraw their paws and increased their heart rate by 50–100 beats a minute. Then one of the assistants entered their cage and fondled the animals while the shock was applied. 'I was certain that the dog would bite the person when shocked,' commented Dr James J. Lynch who took part in the research project, 'but much to my surprise, the petting seemed to make the pain of the shock much less severe.' Contrary to all expectations the heart rates of the fondled animals remained steady or even fell when they were shocked. 'When petted,' Dr Lynch added, 'some of these dogs did not even give the usual flexion response to the shock.' At first he admitted that he found these results 'difficult to understand or believe'. Then he discovered that human contact also improved the blood flow through the dogs' coronary arteries, a response which is of great relevance to the prevention of ischaemic heart disease and anginal pain. So great was this effect for some of the dogs that the entry of a human companion into their room 'was almost as potent a stimulus to coronary flow as violent exercise on the treadmill'.*

*We need company to keep in good heart. Doctors working in intensive care units know that a nurse can check the erratic beating of a patient's heart by the simple act of holding their hand and comforting them.*

*If we are fortunate we may survive throughout our entire lives without the help of high-tech medicine, but there is never a day when we can wisely dispense with the therapy of love. This is a healing medicine everyone can apply, without academic training or formal qualifications. In fact this is the one field in which the amateurs are the only true professionals, for the very word amateur means 'one who loves'.*

# Chapter Twelve:

# OPTIMISM
## *The Fifth b-Attitude of Health*

Doctors should treat their patients with complete impartiality, and yet in practice they generally have their favourites. I certainly am guilty of this offence, and am well aware that I prefer to treat people who have a positive, optimistic outlook. The reason for this bias is quite simple; optimists are more congenial to deal with than pessimists and they also show a much better response to treatment.

Suppose you were about to undergo a dangerous operation or an uncomfortable diagnostic test, such as a lumbar puncture or an arthroscopic examination of the knee. Your response to the procedure would depend on a number of recognised variables, such as the skill of the surgeon, the quality and sterility of his equipment and your level of physical fitness at the time of the operation. But there would be another, frequently overlooked, factor which would play an equally important role in determining your response to treatment: your mental outlook. This was demonstrated recently when a group of patients awaiting cardiac catheterisation was questioned to determine their attitude to the impending investigation. They were offered a series of twelve statements and asked to report on a 5-point scale how closely each comment responded to their personal feelings. Half of the statements were positive, such as 'I was thinking that the procedure could save my life.' The remainder were negative, such as 'I was listening and expecting them to say something bad about my health.' From these replies it was possible to give each patient an Optimism Quotient, a rating which was found to be closely related to the success with which they responded to the treatment. The more negative their outlook the poorer they adapted to the catheterisation.

A similar discovery was made from a study of women undergoing hysterectomy operations at St Thomas's Hospital, London. Some of the patients were treated in the normal way; others, while they were under the anaesthetic, were played a recorded tape message which assured them that the operation was going well and that they would soon be better. The results showed that the women who received the optimistic message recovered quicker and were less likely to suffer fever or gastro-intestinal problems. 'Almost every member of the suggestion group was rated by nurses as having made a better-than-expected recovery', the report stated. Compared with the control group, the women who heard the message of hope and cheer during their operations were five times as likely to be ready to leave hospital within a day of the removal of their stitches.

To make the finest recovery from surgical operations we need to adopt an optimistic outlook. Exactly the same applies to the way we face adversity, sickness, bereavement and ageing. Doctors can tell a lot about their patients' health by looking at their eyes and noting the size of their pupils, the colour of their whites and the puffiness of their lids. More still can be deduced by noting the direction of their gaze. It is said that a healthy fish always looks upstream. The same is true of a healthy human being. The depressed patient and the potential suicide victim stay locked in the gloom of the present because they have little hope that tomorrow will be any better than today. In the same way the hypochondriac dwells on his current symptoms because he views his past and future as being a never-ending succession of aches, pains and medical catastrophes.

To achieve optimum physical and mental health we must look

forward with confidence and hope. If you were given the task of looking around the room where you are now sitting to find as many 'green' objects as you could, you would soon get the impression that the room was bursting with green – the green cushion on the sofa, the green book on the coffee-table, the green lamp shade, the green rug and so on. In the same way if a friend gives us a dramatic account of their recent visit to Namibia, a country we have scarcely heard of previously, we may get the impression during the ensuing days that Namibia has suddenly become the focus of world attention. So it is with all our thoughts. If we set out to see tragedy, we will find examples of misfortune all around us. If we look for sickness, we will discover it lurking in every nook and cranny. If we believe that old age is accompanied by invalidism and loss of memory we will see scores of forgetful, aged cripples, but be blind to the vast number of octogenarians who remain in full possession of their faculties. In this way our thoughts determine our future. If we want to attract success, we must look ahead with confident anticipation. If happiness is our aim, we must focus on matters which evoke a cheerful response. In the same way, if we want to achieve a high level of physical well-being we must think about health rather than about sickness.

By exercising this freedom of choice we control and create our destinies. Either we take a positive outlook and fare well, or we take the pessimistic view and grow sick. In this way our lives are rather like *pointilliste* paintings, made up of an infinite number of tiny dots which in themselves are insignificant, but when grouped together make up the completed picture. Each one of these dots represents a single moment of time – a passing act or a fleeting thought. When we are born we are given a clean brush and a blank canvas on which we are free to paint the portrait of our choice. Each day we add another few dots to our self-created, living image. Heredity provides the canvas, but from birth onwards we choose the colouring and the pattern of the individual daubs of paint. If we always dip our brush into the black pigments – morbid thoughts and negative mental images – the picture we create will be sombre and gloomy. If we sample only a tiny selection of the available colours the self-portrait we construct will be flat and dull. But if we choose to crowd our canvas with bright colours and bold strokes, we will build up a life – dot by dot – which is colourful, lively and fresh.

To this extent we are all self-made men and women. What we do and think today, makes us what we are, do and think tomorrow. As Solomon said: 'As a man thinketh in his heart, so is he.' This is the fundamental truth which shapes our health and moulds our lives.

When Frank Lloyd Wright was born his mother determined that he should become a great architect, and to prepare him for this role she filled his nursery with pictures of grand cathedrals. With these early examples to inspire him, Wright went on to become one of the most famous architects of the twentieth century. When Sir Joshua Reynolds was President of the Royal Academy he refused to give even a passing glance at an inferior painting, in case his own work suffered as a result of even the most fleeting contemplation of the mediocre. In the same way when Veroushka, the famous German model, was asked to reveal her favourite beauty secret she said: 'I just lie on the floor and think about being beautiful.' Whatever we wish to attain – whether it is success, happiness, health or beauty – we must first acquire the appropriate mental set.

Some of my patients are habitually gloomy. If I try to cheer them up by reminding them of the gloriously sunny weather, they will immediately counter by telling me that the heat is playing havoc with their complexion and giving them swollen feet. Even if they won a small fortune on the football pools they would consider themselves unlucky to have won on a week when the dividend was slightly lower than usual, or because the announcement of the prize had attracted a clutch of begging letters. Other patients are the complete opposite and are so programmed to look at the bright side of life that they see a silver lining to every cloud. This difference in outlook conditions their mood and plays a crucial role in determining their health. John Burt, of the University of Maryland, has been a health educator for over a quarter of a century. During this time he has promoted the cause of physical fitness as assiduously as any of his colleagues, but now he is convinced that our most pressing need is for a revision of our mental attitudes and psycho-social habits. 'The chief threat to physical, mental and social well-being in our time,' he says, 'is not heart disease or cancer, not an infectious or environmental agent, not poverty or malnutrition, not human exploitation or economic injustice, not prejudice or even thermo-nuclear war. Rather, the greatest danger to human welfare in our immediate future is . . . what we pre-suppose about ourselves and the human condition in general.'

This may seem a sweeping claim, but in fact it is well supported by medical research which shows that our emotional pre-suppositions affect our life expectation, our immunity to cancer, our response to surgery and also our resistance to stress. Take the simple instance of the way in which we view our health. Some people are martyrs to illness and regard themselves as having a poorer-than-average standard of health. Others make light of their ailments and consider their health to be good. This difference in outlook alone is enough to influence our future expectation of life. This was demonstrated when over 3,500 senior citizens from Manitoba, Canada, took part in a seven-year study. At the beginning of the project the participants were asked to evaluate their own health status. 'For your age,' they were quizzed, 'would you say, in general, your health is excellent, good, fair, poor or bad?' At the same time an objective assessment was made of their health based on hospital records and reports from their family doctors. At the end of the seven-year survey it was found that their initial self-appraisals were a more accurate indication of who would live and who would die than the 'scientific' prognostications of their doctors. Those who regarded their health as poor had a death rate which was three times higher than those who judged their health to be excellent. Even when the medical profession found that the 'health optimists' were in poor physical condition, they showed an above-average survival rate. Obviously what was of prime importance was not what the *doctors* thought about their health, but what *they* themselves thought about their present condition and future expectations. Where longevity is concerned, the Manitoba experiment revealed that it is better to be a sick optimist than a fit pessimist. This positive attitude towards health, the survey showed, is the single most important determinant of life expectancy – with the exception of age itself.

An attitude of optimism also appears to lessen the risk of contracting malignant disease, or failing that, to improve the chance of recovery from cancerous growths, as demonstrated by Dr A. H. Schmale and Dr H. Iker, in their psychoimmunological studies, described in Chapter 6.

Even when malignant growths have become established it can pay to adopt a positive attitude rather than give way to feelings of hopelessness and despair. This was revealed when a computer search was made of the medical literature to unearth all the recorded incidents of spontaneous recovery from cancer. The search produced a total of 400 articles describing a wide variety of 'miracle' cures. In some cases recovery was attributed to a grape juice diet, in others to a visit to Lourdes or a stay in a high altitude resort where the atmosphere was charged with negative ions. But when Dr Elmer Green of the Menninger Foundation studied the case reports he dismissed the curative value of the majority of these remedies. 'The only common factor that I could find,' he reported, 'was a *change of attitude* in the patient prior to the "spontaneous remission", a change involving hope and other positive feelings.'

Dr Carl Simonton, medical director of the Cancer Counselling and Research Center in Dallas, Texas, came to an identical conclusion when he studied the response to treatment of 152 patients from the Travis Air Force Base. Some had a negative attitude to cancer, regarding it as an invariably fatal disease which medicine was powerless to cure and against which the body had no natural defences. Others held a more optimistic view and took comfort from the fact that the human body contains powerful defence mechanisms against malignant growths which enable many people to achieve a permanent victory over cancer. The difference in these two outlooks was clearly reflected in the response to treatment. Those patients whose attitude was positive fared much better than those with a gloomy outlook, only two of whom showed a good response to treatment. But once again the most outstanding finding of the trial was the extent of the therapeutic effect of a healthy mental attitude. This was the conclusion of Dr Simonton himself who reported: 'The most significant finding of the study was that a *positive mental attitude was a better predictor of response to treatment than was the severity of the disease.'*

An attitude of hope can be invaluable in the fight against cancer and can also be a powerful aid to recovery from surgical operations. A group of patients, admitted to hospital for surgical repair of a detached retina, was interviewed to determine their feelings about the impending operation. How well did they trust the surgeon? Were they optimistic that they would regain their sight? Did they feel confident that they would be able to cope after the operation, whatever its outcome? Some were sanguine, others were pessimistic. Not knowing the results of the earlier psychological assessments, the surgeons then recorded the patients' day-by-day responses during the convalescent phase. The two records when compared showed a high degree of concordance, the patients with the highest degree of confidence, trust and hope showing the speediest rates of post-operative recovery.

In the future when patients are scheduled for operations, steps must be taken to prepare their minds for the operating theatre as well as their bodies. Ideally, this mental conditioning should begin in early childhood, so that youngsters are equipped to face not only sickness but also the upheavals and adversities of everyday life. The value of this early training was demonstrated when a group of 141 American students was given a questionnaire to determine their level of optimism. In completing the form they were asked to agree or disagree with a number of statements, which ranged from the extremely optimistic comment, 'I always look on the bright side of things', to the gloomy admission, 'If something can go wrong for me, it will.' Having evaluated their general level of hopefulness, the students were then observed as they went through a particularly stressful four-week period of their academic lives. The results showed that those who were optimistic by nature coped better with the ordeal and suffered fewer tension symptoms – dizziness, tiredness and muscular pains – than those who were habitually pessimistic. The survey also revealed that while there was clear proof that an optimistic outlook promoted physical health, there was no evidence that physical health encouraged people to adopt an optimistic outlook on life.

Happiness is predominantly an attitude of mind rather than a response to external events. For many years psychiatrists were obsessed with the theories of Sigmund Freud and encouraged neurotic patients to believe that they were the hapless victims of early emotional traumas. Now the perspective has been altered and it is more usual to put the responsibility for perpetuating inappropriate mental behaviour on the patient rather than on a variety of outside scapegoats. Cognitive Therapy, the brain-child of Dr Aaron Beck of the University of Pennsylvania School of Medicine, is one of the most promising of these new approaches to psychiatric treatment. After interviewing hundreds of patients with psychological problems, Dr Beck made a fundamental discovery. Thoughts, he realised, are the active instigators of moods rather than their hapless by-products. We do not produce negative thoughts because we are in a gloomy frame of mind, but rather we sink into a state of despondency because we allow our brains to entertain negative thoughts. In the same way we are happy at any particular time because we exercise our right to think positively rather than pessimistically. All our moods are created by our thoughts or 'cognitions'. When people are depressed, according to Cognitive Therapy, it is because their thoughts are dominated by a 'pervasive negativity'. If their distorted outlook is changed their mood will quickly brighten.

These theories were put to the test at the Center for Cognitive Therapy, Pennsylvania, when a series of forty-four severely depressed patients was divided at random into two treatment groups. The first was given a twelve-week course of a highly effective anti-depressant drug. The second received a twelve-week course of personal counselling in Cognitive Therapy, aimed at helping them to identify and eradicate their self-destructive thought patterns. The benefits of this particular approach became apparent within the first few weeks of the experiment and at the end of the trial period it was found that complete recovery was shown by nearly *four* times as many of the counselled patients as those who received the orthodox drug treatment –

which many had to discontinue because of their unpalatable side-effects. Negative thinking can make us depressed, and a switch to a more optimistic outlook can make us well, with greater certainty and safety than drug treatment. If we want to achieve happiness and avoid the pitfalls of psychiatric illness we can do no better than adopt a positive, optimistic outlook, for as Samuel Johnson wrote: 'Hope is, perhaps, the chief happiness this world affords.'

Unfortunately contemporary culture, and contemporary philosophies, do not encourage a spirit of cheerful optimism. I am not surprised that many Russians are dour and glum if they are reared on a diet of Chekovian tragedies and gloomy Tolstoyan novels. In the same way a certain degree of despondency may be understandable in Germans who have come under the influence of the Schopenhauer school of pessimistic philosophy. (Karl Hartmann, a member of this school, was so convinced that love produces more suffering than pleasure that he went to the extremity of suggesting castration as a way of extinguishing sexual desire.) Today, this doctrine of despair is spread by the media, who persist in viewing the world through a black veil of despondency. Even as I write these words I have before me a perfect example of the sad way in which the press distorts the truth. This morning the weatherman announced that Britain had just enjoyed the warmest Christmas period for over forty years. This, one might have expected, would have been taken as a cause for general delight. Because of the unseasonal temperatures the gardens are decked with spring flowers which normally make their appearance weeks later. People are walking about in shirt-sleeves instead of winter coats. Fires are being switched off which is resulting in substantial reductions in fuel bills. The sick and the elderly are flourishing at a time of the year when they would normally be experiencing an increased risk of fatal heart attacks and chest complaints. (Figures released by the Office of Population Censuses and Surveys reveal that during the British winter an extra 8,000 people die for every degree the temperature falls below the seasonal average.) But not one of these heartening facts is mentioned in this morning's paper. Instead it chooses to focus its attention on two minor gripes: the warmer weather has made life difficult for skiers and might aid the spread of influenza. Both of these comments may be factually correct, yet they present a gross and gloomy distortion of the truth.

If the media is to have a healthy influence on public thought and opinion it must spread the good news as well as the bad. It must give cause for optimism as well as despair, and stimulate confidence as well as fear.

For a while *France-Soir*, France's largest circulation newspaper, printed a 'Smiley' motif beside every item of uplifting news. This gave readers the choice of concentrating on cheering events and avoiding, if they wished, the usual witch's brew of murder, rape, scandal, tragedy and disaster. Many publishers doubt the sale-abililty of good news, and yet the *Reader's Digest*, the world's top-selling magazine, proves that the reading public are anxious to read stories of optimism, courage, success, altruism and good cheer.

Negative thoughts – of hatred, fear, resentment and anger – are psychological poisons which can devastate our lives. Othello was destroyed by jealousy, Midas by greed. These were admit-tedly overwhelming passions, and yet there is evidence that our health can be damaged by negative attitudes of far lesser magnitude. The realisation of this fact should condition not only our choice of thoughts, but also our selection of friends, mentors, reading material and leisure-time activities. It should also influence our choice of medical advisers, for the benefit we derive from therapists is measured less by the length of their qualifica-tions than by the breadth of their smiles and the extent of the confidence they generate. This was demonstrated when a group of approximately 200 patients sought medical help for a variety of non-specific symptoms. In each case they complained of feeling 'unwell' and yet there was no discernible organic cause for their complaints. On a totally random basis they then received consultations which were either conducted in a negative manner or in a way which was intended to give them encouragement and cheer. Sometimes they received treatment, at other times not. This in itself appeared to make little difference, for the patients who received a prescription fared scarcely better than those who went untreated. What mattered above all else in the management of these trivial ailments was the attitude of the doctor. When the patients received a *positive* consultation 64 per cent derived substantial benefit, compared with only 39 per cent when they were given a *negative* consultation.

The therapeutic effect of an encouraging bedside manner becomes even more important when we are seriously ill. At these times our morale is reduced and our confidence sapped, so that we long to receive a supportive boost from someone we trust. A clear-cut example of this was provided when patients suffering from bleeding peptic ulcers were divided into two treatment groups. The patients in the first group were told by a doctor that they were about to receive treatment with a highly effective drug which was bound to check their bleeding. The remainder were seen by a nurse who adopted a diffident manner and confessed that the effects of the pills could not be judged since the treatment was still in the experimental stage. In fact the drugs the two groups received were identical, but not so the effects they caused. When the pills were dispensed with enthusiasm, 75 per cent of the patients showed significant healing of their ulcers; a success rate which fell to 25 per cent when the treatment was given in an uninspiring fashion. Once again it appears that the manner of the doctor can be of greater therapeutic significance than the treatment he gives.

Since optimism is of positive survival value to the human race, one would expect that the life-preserving quality of hopefulness would be deeply engrained in the human psyche. This in fact is true, according to psychologists Margaret Matlin and David Stang who, in their book *The Pollyanna Principle*, demonstrate that our innate happiness often triumphs even when we face a baleful army of doomsday predictors, moaning Minnies and Job's comforters. Researchers have found that we operate a rose-tinted mental filter which enables us to take more note of heartening stimuli and events than those which are likely to have a depressing effect. Given a choice, for example, we look at pleasant pictures rather than unpleasant ones. In the same way we tend to transmit good news more readily than bad news. Our memories are equally selective. We recall the pleasurable events in our past lives more accurately and more frequently than the unpleasant happenings. And the more distant the events become the more rosy they appear. The same applies to our judgement, so that we consider agreeable things more likely to occur than disagreeable ones, even when the actual probabilities are the same. This spirit of optimism also pervades our choice of words, to an extent which few of us realise. This was revealed when a count was made of the frequency with which various words were used in 4,500,000 words of magazine text. In all instances words with a positive connotation were used more frequently than their antonyms. Thus 'good' and 'life' were used five times as often as 'bad' and 'death'; and 'love' seven times as frequently as 'hate'. The same selective choice of positive words has been discovered in texts published in French, Spanish, German and Urdu.

Self-appraisal tests confirm that we are at heart basically cheerful creatures. Far more people claim to be optimists than pessimists. And in one survey three-quarters of students rated themselves to be happier than average, while only 8 per cent considered that they enjoyed less than the normal share of happiness. This inherent cheerfulness enables us to cope in times of adversity and helps us to transmute failure into success in our minds if not in reality. A perfect example of this trans-mutation process occurred during the Korean war, when General Oliver Prince Smith was leading the withdrawal of 20,000 US marines who had been trapped by eight divisions of Chinese communists. 'Retreat, hell!' he told war correspondents. 'We're just advancing in a different direction.'

This ability to make a positive appraisal of even the most calamitous situations is one of our saving graces. It is also one of the qualities which makes us most truly human, and I think it highly appropriate that the ancient Greeks should have chosen to call us anthropoids, a word which literally means 'the upward lookers'. If we are to maximise our health and happiness we must always take the upward look and cultivate the habit of optimism. Here are four tried and tested ways of developing an attitude of hope:

- **Take Full Responsibility for Your Life**
  *Doctors frequently find that when patients relinquish their grip on the rudder of destiny they also loosen their hold on life. Psychiatrist Dr Flanders Dunbar illustrated this point by relating the story of two patients who developed coronary disease of equal severity. One took his diagnosis as a challenge, the other as a defeat. The first reacted positively, saying: 'I've got to do something to get well.' The other preferred to make the cardiologist responsible for his future welfare. 'It's up to you now, doctor,' he said resignedly. The first patient recovered, the second died.*

- **Follow the Pollyanna Principle**
  *Some people are programmed in such a way that they always see the black things in life. They will find character flaws in a saint, and when they look at the Mona Lisa will see the cracks in da Vinci's painting but fail to note the Giaconda's facial beauty and enigmatic smile. Others are similarly attuned to take a cheerful view of life, and will find hope in a storm and beauty in a heap of slag. Pollyanna, the youthful heroine of Eleanor Porter's novel, was an irrepressible optimist. She was scheduled to take a cheerful view of everything. Cynics may dismiss this as chocolate-box philosophy, and yet it is practical and highly rewarding. People, things and events are neither wholly black nor totally white. So while it is honest to focus on their negative aspects it is far more beneficial to concentrate on their positive features. Why take a rose and complain of the prick of its thorns when you could be enjoying the sight and scent of its flower? Why moan about a downfall of rain, which you cannot stop, and which you know is vital for the nourishment of the earth? John Ruskin took a sanguine view of the variable British weather. 'Sunshine is delicious,' he wrote, 'rain is refreshing, wind braces us up, snow is exhilarating, there is really no such thing as bad weather, only different kinds of good weather.'*
  *The same applies to our judgement of people, where we should always be quick to praise and slow to condemn. A friend once said of actress Joyce Grenfell: 'Joyce looked for good in everybody and because she looked she found it.'*

In the good times and in the bad – when we are facing illness, bereavement, disappointment, emotional conflict or financial crisis – we will be happier and healthier if we follow the Pollyanna principle and try and find good in every situation.


- ## Eliminate the Negative
  This is the natural corollary of the Pollyanna Principle, for if we manage to suppress the negative aspects of life we automatically bring the positive aspects into greater prominence.

  Anatomists have known for some while that the two sides of the brain serve different functions. Research reveals that this differentiation also applies to the control of human moods. The area at the front of the left hemisphere has been found to deal with positive emotions, while the comparable part of the right hemisphere is involved in the processing of negative emotions. (This applies to right-handed people.) As a result of this differentiation when damage is done to the right side of the brain a feeling of pessimism and fear is provoked, a response often called the 'catastrophic reaction'. Damage to the left side of the brain, on the other hand, gives rise to euphoria and unprovoked outbursts of merriment and laughter. Further confirmation of this arrangement has been provided by electroencephalogram investigations, which show that depressed patients have an increased level of brain activity in the fore part of their right hemispheres.

  Other research has revealed an intriguing, and hitherto unrecognised, consequence of this particular specialisation of brain function. Things seem funnier when they are viewed with our right eye, because messages from this eye are always relayed to the left side of the brain. This has been demonstrated in the laboratory by showing people either sad or funny films. The researchers found that they got the maximum response from a comic movie when they showed it to their subjects' right eyes. Conversely when they wanted to provoke the greatest physiological reaction from an unpleasant or threatening film they discovered that they needed to display it to people's left eyes. Perhaps on the basis of this research we should begin to manufacture 'optimistic spectacles', fitted not with rose-tinted glass, but with a black patch over the left eye and a magnifying lens over the right eye. I have no doubt that before long someone will try this bizarre experiment. Until they do, a practical alternative is to use both eyes to look at the positive side of life and use neither eye to dwell too long on anything which is likely to have a demoralising effect.

Hypochondriacs suffer because they ignore this basic behavioural rule. Rather than dismiss their aches and pains, they make them the centre of their existence. If they recover from the cough which has kept them at death's door for days, they immediately fall prey to terminal chilblains. A much better outlook is the one shown by an elderly patient of mine, who when asked how she is replies: 'Well my back aches and my legs get tired at times, but I myself am very well, thank you.' And if it proves difficult to forget a nagging cough, headache or bout of indigestion, try following Emil Coué's tip and keep repeating to yourself the auto-suggestive phrase 'Ça passe, ça passe, ça passe' (It is going, it is going, it is going).

To check negative thought patterns we also need to forgive and forget. Many people go through life burdened with feelings of guilt and sin. Some are dejected by the constant recollection of past failures. Others are resentful or angry over earlier slights and rebuffs; like Arthur Balfour, the British Prime Minister who when he was ousted as leader of the Conservative Party admitted that he still vividly remembered an earlier slight when 'I was unjustly "complained of" at Eton more than 40 years ago'. These gnawing misgivings are cankers which sap our health and erode our happiness.

One of the great values of the Roman Catholic confessional is that it provides a regular opportunity for emotional catharsis; a time for the admission of errors and the expiation of sins. Even the early pagans recognised the value of this process and held rites at which they sought atonement through sacrifices to their gods. Whatever our religious beliefs we need to set aside time when we can spring-clean our minds of negative thoughts. As Pope said: 'To err is human, to forgive, divine.'

● **Hold On To Hope**

*The great difference between an optimist and a pessimist is that the one has hope and the other has none. The same polarisation of outlook separates the happy person and the depressive patient. So long as we take an optimistic view of the future we continue to mobilise our resources to cope with whatever difficulties and dangers we are experiencing; the moment we give way to despair we cease to fight. Hope is the emotional flywheel which maintains our forward momentum when times are hard. Even if we reach the bedrock of despair we must have the courage to adhere to the principle Shelley expounded in* Prometheus Unbound *and 'hope till Hope creates from its own wreck the thing it contemplates'.*

● **Act Positively**

*Sometimes it is difficult to rid the mind of negative, pessimistic thoughts. On these occasions it is helpful to substitute deeds for thoughts, so that the mind is diverted to more encouraging matters. Here it pays to remember the Pollyanna Principle: that positive, inspiring acts will always have a stronger effect than negative, demoralising acts. This fact is beautifully illustrated in Homer's* Odyssey, *where the story is told of the Greek sailors who were lured on to the rocks by the seductive singing of the Sirens. Ulysses overcame this fatal attraction by lashing his sailors to the mast, which prevented them from acting impetuously but did not curb their overpowering fascination. Orpheus was wiser and adopted a much more effective countermeasure. He sang with such supreme sweetness himself that the Argonauts did not notice the crooning of the Sirens. The launching of a positive counter-attack is always the most effective way of encouraging behavioural change – whether it be overcoming doubts and fears or replacing pessimism with an attitude of hopeful anticipation. As the Chinese say: 'Better light a small candle than curse the dark.'*

# Chapter Thirteen:

# CHEERFULNESS
## *The Sixth b-Attitude of Health*

Many philosophies can only be followed by studious intellectuals who can grasp their theoretical postulates. Others demand a degree of self-denial which can only be maintained by saintly ascetics. Fortunately neither of these strictures apply to the Philosophy of Health. Everyone can follow the seven b-Attitudes of Health whether they are saints or sinners, zany or wise.

Cheerfulness, in particular, is a trait that everyone can express. You do not have to be a genius or an angel to be happy. In fact in some ways an excess of either intellectualisation or piety appear to act as barriers to the enjoyment of simple merriment and fun. Some of the stricter religious orders have even made a virtue of their dolefulness. This certainly applied to the Puritans who thought it was unseemly to laugh and decadent to play. John Bunyan was particularly outspoken on this point in his sermons, preaching against the wantonness of dancing, and the sin of playing hockey on the village green, which he described as 'an ungodly practice'.

Although most churchmen would deny it, Christianity is still afflicted by this puritanical gloom. When last did you see a portrait of Christ, or one of his disciples, laughing? A short while ago the *Church Times* asked its readers to help them find a stained-glass window depicting a smiling saint. Not one was traced. Even ministers seem to feel duty-bound to maintain a sombre air; and yet I am as suspicious of miserable priests as I am of fat doctors and impoverished accountants. If your faith does not make you happy there is something radically wrong with you, or something sadly amiss with your religion.

Within the Jewish tradition there is a much more wholesome attitude towards enjoyment. (As there is towards sex and making money.) In fact the Talmud says that it is the devout Jew's *duty* to take pleasure from the good things in life. 'In the world to come', it warns, 'each of us will be called to account for the good things God put on earth which we refused to enjoy.'

It seems odd that we should ever feel guilty about enjoying life, because there is little doubt that the search for happiness and pleasure is a fundamental human need and an inherent human drive. Even the simplest blob of protoplasm shows an innate tendency to move away from unpleasant stimuli and toward pleasurable stimuli. In humans this hedonistic urge is stronger still and infinitely better organised.

Experiments show that separate parts of our brain are concerned with the perception of different emotions. In one part – the lateral nucleus of the thalamus – we feel anger. When the nerve cells in this area are subjected to electrical stimulation we show a 'rage reaction'. A totally different emotion is located in the region of the brain known as the limbic system. This has been called the 'Pleasure Centre', since its cells are concerned with the perception and relaying of pleasurable stimulation.

The discovery of the Pleasure Centre was made quite fortuitously by psychologist James Olds, while he was carrying out experiments on laboratory rats to see what alerted them from a dormant state. These tests involved the accurate implanting of electrodes in a specific part of the rats' brains, known as the reticular activating system. On one occasion, by mistake, Olds fitted a rat with an electrode needle implanted in the limbic system of its brain instead of its reticular activating system. The slight misplacement produced some wholly unforeseen effects.

Previous experiments had shown that the electrical stimulation of an animal's brain can produce robot-like behaviour. When a tiny current is transmitted to the lateral nucleus of the thalamus, animals become aggressive. When the stimulus is applied to the 'Appestat' centre in the hypothalamus they become ravenously hungry. When impulses are dispatched to their reticular activating centres they become alert. In each of these cases the animals reacted to the electrical stimulation like automatons. They raged, woke up or ate, not because they wanted to, but because they were puppets in the researchers' hands and the appropriate strings were being pulled. But their response was totally different when the stimuli were applied to their limbic systems, where they experienced pleasure. Now they took the initiative and showed a positive craving for the pleasurable stimulation. If the first tingle of pleasure came when they were in the right-hand side of their cage, they would return again and again to this corner in the hope of receiving further titillation. If they were given a self-operating lever, which activated the pleasurable stimulation, they would use this obsessively, operating the on-off switch up to a frenetic 5,000 times an hour.

So great is this instinctive craving for pleasure that even hungry, thirsty or sexually deprived animals will stimulate their Pleasure Centre rather than quench their hunger, slake their thirst or satisfy their sexual longing. And this is not merely a bestial rodent passion, for the same experimental reactions have been demonstrated in fish, guinea-pigs, rabbits, cats, dogs, dolphins, monkeys and even humans. One might reasonably assume that a behavioural tendency which is so widely distributed throughout the animal kingdom must have a positive survival value. Certainly the hedonistic urge is not a recent acquisition of twentieth-century man; and it is surely not without significance that the Pleasure Centre is located in the oldest part of the mammalian brain.

So what role does pleasure play in the promotion of human health and happiness? For centuries it has been accepted that cheerfulness exerts a therapeutic effect. This was recognised by Solomon who said: 'A merry heart doeth good like a medicine.'

209

Laughter has been equally prized for its tonic effect, and was described by Aristotle as 'a bodily exercise precious to health'.

Over the years many doctors have tried to harness the healing powers of humour and light-heartedness. Dr John Kellogg provided 'laughing sessions' at his sanatorium in Battle Creek, Michigan. Here the tired and tense were encouraged to laugh their cares away. A similar technique has been used recently by Dr Vachet of the Paris Institute of Psychology, who teaches students to dispel their anxieties by indulging in uninhibited, rollicking laughter. Better an occasional belly-laugh, Vachet feels, than a constant bellyache.

Other physicians have recommended patients to forget their worries by visiting circuses and vaudeville shows where they can enjoy the humour of comedians and clowns. Thomas Sydenham, probably the greatest clinical physician of the seventeenth century, recommended this treatment and once said: 'The arrival of a good clown exercises a more beneficial influence upon the health of the town than twenty asses laden with drugs.' A century later a doctor gave this advice to a melancholic patient suffering from dyspepsia. After examining him and finding nothing seriously amiss he said: 'All you need is a good hearty laugh. Go and see Grimaldi.' 'Alas!' replied the unhappy patient, 'I *am* Grimaldi.' Which confirms the fact that comedians, even those with the comic genius of a gifted clown like Joey Grimaldi, are not always able to share the happiness that they so ably transmit to their audiences.

Notwithstanding the irony of the Pagliacci situation, when a clown has to make an audience laugh at a time when his own heart is breaking, there is no doubt that a skilled comedian like Grimaldi, Charlie Chaplin, Buster Keaton or Bob Hope can do more to promote the mental and physical well-being of a nation than an entire college of physicians. David Kaminsky, the son of Russian Jewish immigrants, always wanted to be a doctor. But his father's New York tailoring business provided too little money to send David to university let alone to medical school. So the youngster left school and made a living working in a soda fountain. Eventually he found a way of helping people which did not involve detailed medical knowledge – he became an entertainer. Under the stage name of Danny Kaye his versatile performances gave joy to millions. 'I think I've made people happy by making them laugh,' the would-be doctor wrote, 'and I think that when you make someone laugh you're giving him medicine.'

One of the medicinal values of laughter is that it helps to dispel tension. A number of leading philosophers and psychiatrists have written serious treatises on the psychology of laughter, including Plato, Aristotle, Kant, Bergson, Freud, Huxley and Koestler. All agree that the physical act of laughter is accompanied by a sudden release of tension. Part of the art of the comedian, in fact, is to build up a degree of tension and then release it in a sudden outburst of laughter. The same art is sometimes displayed in horror films, when perhaps a sequence is shown of a terrified youngster hiding in a room from a vicious assailant. The anxiety mounts when soft, stealthy footsteps are heard approaching the room. The audience sits rigidly on the edge of their seats when a vase falls to the ground in the corridor outside, and they catch their breath *en masse* when the door begins to swing slowly open. But the tension is dissipated in a sudden outburst of laughter and relief when the stealthy entrant is found to be, not the homicidal maniac everyone expected, but a cuddly Persian cat.

The tension-relieving effect of laughter is particularly important during times of stress, which is why some of the finest humour springs from the concentration camps, ghettos and battlefields. In the good times we laugh from pleasure, in the bad times we laugh from sheer necessity. During the blitz on London a shared sense of cockney humour helped to maintain public morale, and I still have a vivid recollection of some of the jokes which circulated during those anxious days. Typical of the genre was the oft-repeated story of the man who was rescued from a completely devastated house. When the recovery team finally burrowed through the rubble they found him with his trousers down in what remained of the downstairs cloakroom – roaring with laughter. 'I just pulled the chain and the house fell down,' he guffawed.

During World War One the plight of the British tommies was

more extreme and their humour correspondingly sicker. Some even made jokes about their comrades, whose dead bodies were draped on the barbed wire like washing hanging out to dry. They laughed, not through callousness, but to protect themselves from being consumed with horror and grief and because no amount of tears could restore the lives of their fallen comrades. At times like these, said Henri Bergson, the French philosopher, laughter provides a 'momentary anaesthesia of the heart'.

There are times when tensions are generated within our bodies – from anger, lust or fear – which cannot easily be defused by appropriate action. It is not always desirable to punch your boss on the nose when he irritates you, rape your neighbour when they sensually arouse you, or scream in terror when you are trapped in a broken-down lift. When these socially inappropriate outlets are denied us, we can often find relief in laughter. This cathartic mechanism was first described by the English philosopher Herbert Spencer in 1863, who pointed out that when emotional energy cannot find release in one direction, it may sometimes be defused as laughter. In this way we can give harmless vent to pent-up anger, embarrassment, anxiety, fear or shame.

Freud agreed that humour acts as a valuable safety valve. We try to maintain the outward appearance of being civilised creatures, but to do so we must suppress our animal instincts which are always seething below the surface. Every now and again the thin veneer of civilisation cracks and we lose our hard-won dignity and composure. When we are at a smart dinner party and our decorous hostess gives vent to an unintended belch we give an embarrassed titter, and we laugh uproariously when the elegantly robed judge stumbles and dislodges his wig as he solemnly enters court. On these occasions the mask of decorum slips and for a brief while we stop pretending that we are model citizens and are content to be our honest-to-goodness animal selves. In Freudian terms this laughter arises when the pent-up animal energies of the id find a way around the inhibiting barrier erected by the conscience or superego. This discharge eases tension and prevents us from taking life too seriously or becoming over-impressed with our own importance. When uti-lised in this way laughter becomes a valuable method of psychological prophylaxis. As one psychiatrist observed: 'I've seldom been called upon to help a person who had a sense of the ridiculous, and I've *never* had to treat anyone who could really laugh at himself.'

Laughter also exerts a powerful socialising force, which is similar in purpose to the appeasement gestures of monkeys. When a macaque monkey encounters a neighbouring tribe on neutral ground it indicates its peaceful intentions by baring its teeth, smacking its lips and rolling its head from side to side, looking in the process remarkably like a little old man chuckling over a *Punch* cartoon. We use very similar forms of non-verbal communication. When we greet strangers with a smile we give an assurance that our intentions are wholly benign. When we give an audible laugh we signal to everyone within earshot that there is no danger on the horizon, so it is safe for members of the group to relax, let their hair down and enjoy themselves in a carefree, uninhibited way. This explains why laughter is so infectious. 'Laugh and the world laughs with you' the saying goes, and by its very nature laughter helps to break down the barriers between people and encourages feelings of group unity. You cannot be sure that a barking dog won't bite, but you can be reasonably confident that a laughing man won't turn and stab you in the back. So you relax and feel at ease within his company. In this way, says Victor Borge, 'Laughter is the shortest distance between two people.'

This principle could well be employed on a global basis and there is little doubt that we would do more to further the cause of international brotherhood if we sent comedians as our ambassadors to foreign countries rather than teams of sober diplomats. If we wish to further the cause of world peace we should take to throwing custard pies rather than Molotov cocktails.

Cheerfulness has its outlet in laughter and is also expressed in play. All animals show a natural tendency to play games. Dogs delight in chasing after a stick. Porpoises will play for hours with an isolated feather from a pelican's back. Elephants and chimpanzees in zoos derive fiendish pleasure from squirting jets of water over unsuspecting visitors. Sea-lions held in captivity will play 'ball' with pieces of floating debris, and have been known to build up a cache of 'toys' in rock clefts; returning to the hide-out to select a favourite plaything whenever they begin to feel bored. But the most popular and universal of all animal games is mock fighting, especially to capture and hold a selected vantage point. First one animal takes proud possession of the targeted high ground, then it is toppled by rivals who briefly establish their own dominance. This is an exact counterpart of the popular childhood playground game known as 'King of the Castle'.

Remarkably enough, although we recognise a play instinct in children and animals, we are very slow to acknowledge that human adults have an equal need to play. This was a major finding of the Wolfenden Committee Report on *Sport and the Community*, commissioned by the Central Council of Physical Recreation. 'Man needs play,' the report concluded. 'In the form of a game, a sport or an outdoor activity of some kind, it is desirable in itself, for its own sake as a valuable element in a full and rounded life.' But what requirement does this need satisfy? At present we know a considerable amount about the physiology of work, but precious little about the physiology of play. It is accepted that all work and no play makes Jack a dull boy; and it is generally agreed that a dearth of play limits growth and creativity.

Little girls, even in a world struggling to avoid sexual stereotyping, train themselves to become mothers by playing with dolls; while little boys prepare themselves for their generally more combative futures by learning to climb, fight and wrestle. The skills of cooking and handiwork are acquired in much the same way. In fact Plato recommended that miniature tools should be given to three-year-olds to prepare them to become builders in later life.

Within the relaxed world of fantasy and play we can safely learn new skills, overcome old fears and explore new territories. To make use of this schooling the Farleigh Mental Hospital, near Bristol, has created an adventure playground 'to stimulate patients to explore their potential'. A similar training ground has been established at Ulm in Germany, where psychiatrist Tobias Brocher has set up a 'play school for parents'. Here grown-ups are encouraged to use the activities of the kindergarten – finger

214

painting and clay modelling – to overcome their emotional frustrations and psychological hang-ups.

When we play we enter a world of light-heartedness and fun which is far removed from the formality and rigidity of our everyday lives. In his classical study *Homo Ludens*, the historian Johan Huizinga said: 'The play mood is one of rapture and enthusiasm . . . A feeling of exaltation and tension accompanies the action, mirth and relaxation follow.' These mirth-related changes – elation, diversion, happiness and relaxation – add enormously to the sum of human well-being. This was demonstrated by psychiatrist Erik Erikson when he made a special study of a group of children. Thirty years later when they had matured he investigated them again and discovered that the adults living the most interesting, fulfilling lives were the ones who had managed to keep a sense of playfulness at the centre of their lives. This twentieth-century study provides experimental support for a theory propounded by Greek philosophers over 2,000 years ago. 'What then is the right way of living?' asked Plato. His disciples might have provided scores of answers to this rhetorical question. Some might have suggested that life should be lived in accordance with strict ethical principles. Others that every moment should be spent as if it was our last on earth. But Plato gave none of these obvious replies. To his way of thinking there was only one answer to the question he posed. 'Life,' he said, 'should be lived as play.'

It may appear far-fetched to place such importance on cheerfulness and play, and yet recent medical research has provided considerable evidence that happiness does indeed play an important role in promoting health and preventing serious disease. Tests show that people who habitually use humour as a way of coping with the stresses and strains of life have higher-than-average levels of salivary immunoglobulin A (IgA), the antibody which provides protection against infections of the upper respiratory tract. Equally impressive are the tests performed on university students which show that watching a comedy programme on television leads to an immediate boost in the levels of salivary IgA. It is possible that this improved immunity may afford protection against the development of cancer, which would provide backing for the bold statement made by British surgeon Sir Heneage Ogilvie: 'The happy man never gets cancer.'

Happiness may also be an antidote to rheumatism. This was suggested by the experience of Norman Cousins, editor of the *Saturday Review*, who developed ankylosing spondylitis, a crippling disease which causes progressive stiffening of the spine and sometimes also of the peripheral joints. Cousins contracted the disease after a particularly exhausting business trip to Russia, and was quickly bedridden and barely able to move his neck, arms, fingers and legs. The prognosis was grim and he was given no more than a one in 500 chance of recovery. Since the medical profession appeared powerless to help, Cousins decided to take greater responsibility for the management of his case. 'Up to that time,' he wrote, 'I had been more or less disposed to let the doctors worry about my condition. But now I felt a compulsion to get into the act. It seemed clear to me that if I was to be that "one case in 500" I had better be something more than a passive observer.'

How had the disease started, he asked himself? Knowing a little about the biochemistry of stress, he surmised that his heavy work-load and business worries might have exhausted the capacities of his over-extended adrenal glands. He knew that frustration and prolonged emotional tension could cause adrenal depletion. Could the reverse be true, he wondered? Could positive emotions have a regenerative influence on his hormonal system? Was it possible that 'love, hope, faith, laughter, confidence and the will to live had therapeutic value'? To put this theory to the test Cousins stopped taking pain-killers and anti-inflammatory drugs and embarked on a regimen of rest, megadoses of vitamin C and faith. But the main plank of his treatment programme was laughter. To jolt his laughter buds into action he watched old Marx Brothers' films and re-runs of the TV programme *Candid Camera*. For added variety a nurse would occasionally read extracts from a comedy book. At the start of the experiment Cousins was in great pain and he felt that his body had been run over by a truck. Then the merriment therapy began to take effect. 'I made the joyous discovery that 10 minutes of genuine belly laughter had an anaesthetic effect and would give me at least two hours of pain-free sleep.' The medical staff also noted that the laughter sessions produced a small but sustained drop in the patient's erythrocyte sedimentation rate, a blood test which gives an estimate of the activity of a wide range of inflammatory disease processes.

Of far greater importance were the accompanying improvements in the patient's physical performance. After eight days of rollicking laughter Cousins could move his thumbs without pain. Two weeks later he was able to join his wife on a sunshine holiday and stand unaided in the surf. A week later he even jogged for a minute or two. Gradually his movements returned and he was able to return to his full-time work with the *Saturday Review*. Twelve years later, apart from occasional twinges in his knees he was totally free of pain and able to ride a horse and play tennis. Only then did he think it appropriate to write a full account of his experiences, which he called *Anatomy of an Illness*. This remarkable book has had a profound effect on the medical profession. Several American hospitals are now employing laughter and play as standard therapies. At the Saratoga Institute, Saratoga Springs, Dr Joel Goodman has launched 'The Humour Project' to explore the therapeutic use of laughter. As an adjunct he also publishes a quarterly magazine *Laughing Matters*, which carries advice to help readers develop their humour skills and attitude of cheerfulness. Several nurses have made their contribution by forming a group called 'Nurses for Laughter' with the sole aim of promoting the use of humour therapy by the health-care professions.

Cheerfulness is a life-preserving elixir. This was one of the prime findings of the forty-year study carried out by researchers from Harvard University Medical School which was described in Chapter Eight. This revealed that men who are happy with their jobs, marriages and leisure-time activities enjoy lives which are longer and healthier than average. Not surprisingly it was discovered that men who were unhappy about their lives had a surfeit of chronic health problems. These negative attitudes also influenced their life expectancy, for a high percentage of the men who employed unhealthy coping strategies – anxiety, depressive withdrawal, stereotyped thinking – were either in poor health or dead before they were fifty-five. But of the men who showed mature ways of dealing with adversity – humour, happiness, social support and adaptability – only one was in poor physical health by the time they reached the age of fifty-five and none had died. The moral, according to Dr Vaillant, who co-ordinated the study, is 'Be happy, you'll live longer.' In this world he who laughs, lasts.

But how easy is it to follow Dr Vaillant's advice? Everyone would surely like to be happier, but can a person who has been melancholic from childhood onwards turn themselves into a cheerful bundle of fun, with the ease with which the fairy godmother converted a pumpkin into a golden coach for Cinderella's journey to the palace? To answer this fundamental question psychologist Michael W. Fordyce, of the Edison Community College, Fort Myers, Florida, exposed a group of approximately one hundred university students to a structured programme of happiness training. The course was based on the findings of over 300 happiness research studies. These previous investigations had identified a number of factors which are conducive to a permanent mood of cheerfulness as distinct from purely fleeting states of happiness. Some of these factors – such as improved health, higher income, sustained marital bliss, raised job and social status – were thought to be beyond the immediate control of most individuals and so were omitted from the Edison training programme. Of the factors which remained, fourteen were selected as being closely related to long-term contentment and emotional well-being. Each of these characteristics – described as 'The Fourteen Fundamentals of Happiness' – can be acquired by appropriate social-skill training and behavioural re-education. They are:

a)  Pursue a busy, active life
b)  Engage in productive, meaningful work
c)  Adopt a more organised, planned life-style
d)  Set goals which are realistic rather than over-demanding
e)  Think positively and optimistically
f)  Eliminate negative feelings and attitudes as far as possible

g) Avoid needless worry
h) Devote adequate time to social activities
i) Develop a warm, outgoing personality
j) Establish satisfying close personal relationships
k) Put a high priority on being happy
l) Learn to live in the present
m) Be yourself
n) Aim to develop a 'healthy' personality

The first ten of these factors deal with attitudes – work commitment, sociability and optimism – which have been considered in earlier chapters of this book. The last four relate more specifically to the pursuit of happiness and will be discussed later in this chapter. Together they provided the basis of the highly successful Edison training programme, which helped eight out of every ten students to attain a happier outlook on life. In 6 per cent of cases the happiness gains were described as 'extreme' and in 30 per cent as 'much greater'.

These results help to counter the arguments of the killjoys who say that cheerfulness cannot be acquired. In their view happiness, like good fortune, either comes our way or it avoids us. Chasing happiness, they say, is like chasing an unruly puppy; the more you pursue it the more elusive it becomes. To others the idea of seeking happiness is artificial and contrived. To them happiness should be as spontaneous as an earthquake, as elusive as a butterfly and as ephemeral as a rainbow. While this may apply to sudden moments of unpremeditated ecstasy, it is certainly not true of long-continued moods of cheerfulness which can undoubtedly be acquired.

As James Olds discovered, and countless other research workers have confirmed, the pursuit of happiness is a fundamental occupation of all animals. Just as seeing is the basic function of the eye, so the search for happiness is one of the basic functions of human existence. Far from being a purely selfish occupation, the quest for happiness adds to the sum of human well-being by reducing tension, spreading joy and fostering warm, social relationships. Cheerfulness can be induced by adopting the following practices:

● **Keep Smiling**

*Anyone can contort their face into a smile, a gesture which requires little effort and no skill. (The signal is produced by the co-ordinated contraction of fifteen facial muscles, chief of which is the zygomatic major, the muscle involved in raising the upper lip.) The immediate effect of creating a smile is to make the face appear more beautiful. This was demonstrated by the German anthropologist Hans Hass, who took a series of films with a concealed movie camera and was struck by the beautifying effects of a smile. In his book* The Human Animal *he tells how he filmed a Chinese woman during a fit of fury when her face looked positively repulsive. Ten minutes later she was smiling and her face, while not classically beautiful, was positively attractive. 'This signal,' he marvelled, 'beautifies any face.'*

*Smiling is also the finest way of making friends and influencing people, as every politician knows. The popularity and charisma of many US Presidents, such as Roosevelt, Kennedy, Eisenhower and Reagan, have seemed to be closely related to their warm, infectious smiles which endeared them to the American people. (In 1908 a reporter spent a week in the White House with Teddy Roosevelt and estimated that he laughed heartily an average of 100 times a day!) In the same way the cold, compassionless public images of world leaders like Margaret Thatcher and President Mitterrand of France appear less closely linked to their true natures than to their predominantly serious unsmiling expressions.*

*Every time we smile, we benefit personally from the medicine of cheerfulness and also help to spread the therapy of happiness to others. And the mood of conviviality we convey with our smiles spreads as rapidly as the most infectious disease, for every person we cheer with a smile is likely to infect another dozen with their light-heartedness. This beneficial chain reaction was recognised by the prophet Buddha who said: 'Thousands of candles can be lighted from a single candle, and the life of the candle will not be shortened. Happiness never decreases by being shared.'*

*Several attempts have been made to instigate smiling campaigns, in which recruits are encouraged to go through the day spreading smiles rather than scowls. In America one of the* most influential movements has been called Smile Power Inc. In France the major crusade, led by philosopher André Moreau, has been dubbed Jovialisme. But the 'Share a Smile' policy does not need to be institutionalised. Smiling is a sanitary practice and a social duty which every responsible citizen should perform. Some authorities, like Havelock Ellis, would even consider that laughter was 'a religious exercise', since it leads to an 'expansion of the soul'. This certainly is the view of the Zen Buddhists, who regard laughter as an essential ingredient of enlightenment.

- Act As If
Many people feel that it is bogus to go through the day spreading artificial smiles, and some scientists have even thought it necessary to teach us how to differentiate false smiles from the genuine variety. (The true grin according to Dr Paul Ekman of the University of California crinkles the eyes and produces a symmetrical lift to the corners of the mouth, whereas the phoney smile rarely involves the eyes and produces a wry expression with one corner of the mouth – usually the left in right-handed subjects – higher than the other.) But in the long run the body makes very little distinction between spontaneous and induced cheerfulness. Whether the state of happiness is thrust upon us, or achieved by an act of will, its physiological effects are the same – muscular relaxation, arterial dilation, flushed skin and sparkling eyes.

This was the lesson taught by Emil Coué and his followers in the school of Auto-suggestive Therapy. If we act happy, we will feel happy. If we maintain a glum expression on our face and sit in the drooping posture of defeat we are likely to feel sad. But if we straighten our backs, put a smile on our lips and a sparkle in our eyes, we will soon begin to feel as cheerful as we look. This method of inducing cheerfulness was neatly described by C. Harry Brooks in The Practice of Autosuggestion: 'Happiness, you say, cannot be ordered like a chop in a restaurant. Like love its very essence is freedom. This is true; but like love it can be wooed and won.'

- ## Take Responsibility for Your Own Happiness
*The art of happiness lies in making felicitous choices. Like Pollyanna we can choose to look at the bright things of life or we can decide to focus our attention on the things which are negative, morbid or glum. Often our inability to be happy stems from our failure to make the appropriate choice or even to recognise that we have the power to control our own emotional destiny. All too often we allow others to manipulate our moods. Perhaps we are driving along a delightful country lane. The scenery is idyllic, the weather superb and we feel at peace with the world. Then a reckless driver hurtles towards us on the wrong side of the road. We are forced to take evasive action to avoid a crash and our restful state of mind is shattered. That much is understandable. But why do we seethe with anger for the remainder of the day over the thoughtless behaviour of that one reckless driver? Why do we allow a total stranger to dominate our thinking and destroy our happiness?*

*John Powell, the American Jesuit, tells the story of a man who always bought his daily newspaper from a vendor who was both irascible and rude. However abrasive and ill-mannered the shopkeeper became the man refused to be provoked and always responded with politeness and courtesy. 'Why do you stay so pleasant and cool?' a friend asked him with amazement. 'Why should I allow his bad temper to pull me down?' he replied. That is the response of maturity, given by someone who has learned to be the master of his moods.*

*Although it is sometimes difficult to avoid mirroring the moods of other people, we must accept that at all times we have the freedom to either share their misery or express our cheerfulness. As Epictetus said: 'If a man is unhappy it must be his own fault; for God made all men to be happy.' Unfortunately some people exercise this choice adversely and regularly opt to take the glum view. I see this as the root cause of the habitual melancholia of several of my patients. I was trying to make one elderly man happy by reminding him of some of the bright spots in his life; but he refused to be cheered up. When his treatment was over I bade him farewell and wished him a happy weekend. To which he replied: 'I'm afraid I can't. I've made other plans.' He* was exercising his right to control his mental attitude, but in a way which was wholly detrimental to his happiness and health.

The early Greek philosophers gave considerable thought to the pursuit of happiness. In *Nichomachean Ethics* Aristotle gave a summary of their views. There were, he said, three theories concerning the origins of happiness. The first two theories were fatalistic and held that happiness occurred as a matter of chance, or as the gift of God. The third theory considered that happiness arose as a result of training, learning and the formation of right habits. Current psychological knowledge would support this belief. Happiness may be considered the gift of God, but it is a gift which – like other inherent talents such as singing, painting or piano playing – can be developed or ignored.

## • Have Fun

If we are cold we switch on a fire. If we are lonely we speak to a friend. In the same way when we are unhappy we should turn immediately to activities which we know will raise our mood. Like Norman Cousins we should follow a conscious policy of attracting cheerfulness – by listening to our favourite amusing records, reading humorous books, looking at Thurber cartoons, watching Marx Brothers' films or viewing comedy TV shows. The Greeks were very concerned about the well-being of people who could not laugh, whom they called the *agelasti*. We should be equally solicitious about the health of our contemporary *agelasti*, who have somehow forfeited the God-given gift of cheerfulness and must be retrained to laugh by regular exposure to mirth-provoking stimuli.

## • Find Time to Play

Alfred the Great advised his Anglo-Saxon countrymen to divide their day into three sections: 'Eight hours for work, eight hours for play, and eight hours for sleep.' Today most people find adequate time for work and sleep, but very few allot sufficient time for play. Nowadays we have an enormous leisure industry which provides us with a bewildering array of play substitutes, such as fruit machines, cinemas, casinos, night-clubs, theatres, television, video films and computer games. These provide the toys, but cannot create the play. Even when we do indulge in games we invariably limit ourselves to activities such as bridge and tennis which have strict boundaries and formal rules. But organised games such as these, because of their rigid framework, make a very poor substitute for the unfettered play enjoyed by children and animals.

We all need to let our hair down from time to time to give vent to our animal high spirits and to forget our responsibilities and cares. And the more arduous and exacting our work, the greater our need for play. The young wife of General Andoche Junot was a regular visitor to Malmaison, the country retreat outside Paris where Napoleon and his staff retired to relax during the height of their military campaigns. On one of these visits she was surprised to discover the French Emperor leading his officers in an impromptu game of tag. 'There was the conqueror of the world,' she recalled, 'his jacket on the ground, running like a schoolboy.' Napoleon had obviously discovered the cathartic power of play.

Many adults find it difficult to be frivolous, unless they can claim to be entertaining a child or household pet. The fundamental secret of joviality is to give free expression to your feelings in movement – by swinging from the branch of a tree when the mood takes you, splashing in the sea, chasing after a falling leaf, or aping the movements of a flock of gambolling lambs. All the words we use to express states of unsophisticated pleasure – gaiety, vivacity, merry-making, animal spirits and jollity – imply an element of spontaneous movement. The same is true of similes such as 'merry as a cricket', 'happy as a sandboy' and 'gay as a lark'. To this extent cheerfulness can be considered the reward for being actively involved in the inconsequential and unsophisticated aspects of life.

- ## Keep Congenial Company
Humour is always intensified when it is shared. Research has shown that people are five times as likely to smile when the sun is shining than on dull days; but the presence of company is an

*even more powerful inducer of cheerfulness, according to tests conducted by two social psychologists from Cornell University. Irrespective of whether the day is bright or cloudy, we are more than seven times more inclined to smile when we are holding a conversation, or greeting a friend, than when we are on our own.*

*The sound of other people laughing is particularly infectious, so much so that one French psychiatrist now 'treats' his depressed patients by exposing them to the sound of recorded laughter, knowing that however miserable they happen to be they will soon overcome their 'blues' and join in the communal merriment. This is why comedians sometimes seed their audiences with a stooge who is employed to lead the laughs, and why the producers of comedy radio and TV programmes often superimpose canned laughter to their shows in the certain knowledge that this will increase the listener's response. (Tests conducted at Trinity College, Dublin show that students not only laugh more heartily when taped laughter is added to TV shows, but that they also rate the doctored shows as being funnier than when they were viewed without the added laughter.)*

*If we are to benefit from the therapy of shared amusement we must take part in more group activities, such as amateur theatricals, choir practices, sports clubs, dances, parties, coach outings, fund-raising events and charity dinners to counteract our increasing time spent in solitary leisure pursuits. Arnold Bennett once wrote: 'The tragedy of existence . . . lay in the failure of communities to organise themselves for pleasure.'*

*To the puritanically minded this may seem an unduly hedonistic goal, but in fact we are never employed more innocently, nor more helpfully, than when we are spreading happiness. This is a fundamental Muslim belief, clearly stated in the Koran: 'He deserves Paradise who makes his companions laugh.' This must be one of the most delightful ways of securing entry through the pearly gates and gaining access to a heaven where places of honour must surely be reserved for comic geniuses like Mark Twain, James Thurber, S. J. Perelman, Charlie Chaplin, Buster Keaton, Groucho Marx and the circus clowns Grimaldi, Coco and Brock.*

- **Do Not Take Life, or Yourself, Too Seriously**
  *Depending on how you view it, life can be fun or a deadly serious sequence of tasks, responsibilities and disappointments. Democritus of Abdera found the world's failings and foibles an endless source of merriment. He was always laughing at the human predicament, so much so that Hippocrates was consulted and asked to comment on his sanity. After studying his case and investigating his history the great physician pronounced that Democritus, far from being unhinged, was actually the very picture of health. But we need to keep a balance, as no doubt Democritus did, between being excessively flippant about things of great gravity and being too serious over matters of lesser importance.*

  *Abraham Lincoln knew how to maintain this proper sense of proportion. On one occasion during the height of the American Civil War he insisted on reading an extract from a humorous skit by Artemus Ward as a prelude to one of the meetings of his War Cabinet. His colleagues were incensed by his apparent flippancy, and one admitted afterwards that he nearly quit the meeting in disgust. But Lincoln read on, and when the sketch was finished he said: 'Gentlemen, why don't you laugh? With the fearful strain that is upon me night and day if I did not laugh I should die – and you need the medicine as much as me.' The President was undoubtedly right. We all need the medicine of laughter and particularly so when times are hard; for it is when we have least to laugh about that we have the greatest need to laugh.*

  *But most of all we need to laugh at ourselves, an exercise which can do more to dispel our anxieties and put our problems into perspective than months of psychotherapeutic counselling.*

- **Be Yourself**
  *When Michael Fordyce quizzed his students who had undergone the 'Fourteen Fundamentals' training programme, he found that one of the factors which had done most to help them achieve a more cheerful outlook was the instruction to 'Be yourself'. (The other most helpful items of advice proved to be 'Avoid needless worry' and 'Think positively and optimistically.') We cannot be*

*relaxed and happy if we are constantly hiding behind a mask and acting the role of the stranger other people imagine us to be, or would like us to become. So long as we maintain this deceit we must be constantly anxious and on our guard in case our mask slips and we become exposed as impostors. But if we are content to be ourselves we can relax, for since we have nothing to hide we can act freely, naturally and spontaneously. Freud's patients suffered because they allowed the straightjacket of the superego to imprison the lively animal energies of the id. If we are to find true peace of mind and genuine happiness we must recapture the naturalness and spontaneity we knew as children.*

- ## Give a High Priority to Being Happy
  *Anyone can be cheerful who follows these principles providing they are prepared to make the quest for happiness one of their major goals. Some will fail because they are too busy making money to take time off to enjoy themselves with their friends. Others will not be prepared to take responsibility for their emotional well-being, but will allow others to manipulate their moods. Many will be too shy to smile at strangers; still more will be too repressed to permit themselves the freedom to indulge in uninhibited fun and games. But everyone who sincerely wants to achieve a more cheerful outlook, and is prepared to work to develop this inherent talent, will have no trouble in finding the happiness they seek. This was the assurance of the poet Ella Wheeler Wilcox, a leading exponent of the pragmatic school of psychology known as New Thought. 'If you are seeking health, wealth, usefulness, skill in any direction,' she said, 'there is nothing, and no one, who can hinder your attainment of the coveted boon, if you are willing to work and wait.'*

Chapter Fourteen:

# CONTENTMENT
## *The Seventh b-Attitude of Health*

We live in the Age of Discontent. Every day we are bombarded by advertisements which encourage us to be dissatisfied with what we have and to yearn for something newer, bigger, faster or simply more expensive. At one time we aimed to keep up with the Joneses, now we feel the need to surpass them.

This insatiable yearning provides a constant source of frustration and inter-group rivalry. Archaeologists have found little evidence of warfare among people living during the late Ice Age. Violent conflicts arose at a much later date – some 6,000 to 8,000 years ago – when human tribes built permanent agricultural settlements and started to develop the concept of personal possessions and land ownership. Then they began to differentiate 'mine' from 'yours' and developed a growing eagerness to struggle and fight to protect and extend their material assets. Today there are still some nomadic tribes who despise the acquisition of personal wealth. The Marsh Arabs of Southern Iraq, for instance, despise trade and have little regard for personal wealth, preferring to judge people on their 'character, virtues and lineage'. But among the materialistic communities of the West it is customary to judge people by the cars they drive, the clothes

228

they wear, the homes they own, the clubs they belong to and the assets they possess. We judge people by what they *have* rather than by what they *are*. When they are alive the question we ask is, 'How much are they worth?' When they die we want to know, 'How much did they leave?'

The struggle to maintain our place in the acquisitive rat race is a major cause of contemporary stress. The more we have, the more we have to worry about. If we build up a portfolio of shares we have to take care that they do not suffer a catastrophic drop in value. If we fill our homes with expensive paintings and antique silver we have more to fear from burglars. If we acquire a second home in the country we have to worry about vandals, leaking roofs and frost damage. As our assets increase, so do our concerns. Even the natives of Polynesia recognise this, for they have a saying: 'He who has a big canoe, has big problems.'

Eventually these material possessions can become a liability rather than an asset. The rare white elephant is a much prized object in Thailand, where it is regarded as a 'royal' animal. Examples are normally presented as gifts to the reigning monarch. They are not permitted to work and must be fed on food befitting a member of the royal family. In the past when the king of Siam wanted to chastise one of his courtiers he gave him a white elephant as a present. Ostensibly this was a generous gift, but in practice it was a severe financial punishment since the costly status symbol could not be put to practical use and had to be given royal care and attention. The possessions of many people today – the heavily mortgaged homes and the luxury cars bought on expensive hire-purchase agreements – can be equally crippling 'white elephants'.

If we have a consuming passion today, it is for consuming. Like magpies we try to fill our nests with useless baubles. In the struggle to acquire more consumer goods we enter deeper and deeper into debt. The Bible, the Koran, the Rabbinic scholars and the early Christian church all forbade the practice of money-lending, but we have developed usury into a lucrative industry. Polonius advised his son, 'Neither a borrower nor a lender be'. We prefer to teach our children the fundamental tenet of consumerism: 'Live now, pay later.' As a result thousands of youngsters are running up credit card debts that they are under duress to repay. They no longer run the risk of being thrown into a debtors' prison if they default, but they are subjected to the enslavement of anxiety and escalating financial responsibilities. And for what good purpose? Certainly there appears to be no correlation between happiness and material wealth. In the words of an ancient Sinhalese proverb: 'He who is happy is rich, but it does not follow that he who is rich is happy.' This is borne out by an American survey which reveals that approximately 80 per cent of people who commit suicide are comparatively prosperous.

Money can buy medical treatment but not health; expensive clothes but not beauty; a splendid house but not a home; books but not wisdom; luxury food but not a healthy appetite. And material wealth, unlike wealth of character, is exceedingly ephemeral. Expensive cars rust, beautiful china breaks, anti-quarian books stain, television sets age, cashmere coats become moth-eaten and stylish kitchen fitments date. Their very imper-manence causes us anxiety. And when we die, we know that we will have to leave behind the status symbols which we have laboured so hard to amass. After all, as an ancient Spanish proverb reminds us: 'There are no pockets in a shroud.'

By making wealth our goal we pervert our sense of values. We judge objects not by their quality, usefulness or aesthetic appeal, but by their market valuation. This was convincingly demon-strated by Antoine Pinay when he was Finance Minister of France. He invited a number of shopkeepers to cut their Camembert cheeses in half. The left halves they were asked to price normally, the right were deliberately made several francs more expensive. In nearly every case purchasers coming into the shops chose to buy the most costly cheese on offer, working on the false assumption that the expensive things in life must be better than those which have a lower monetary valuation. Such is our distorted sense of values.

Another drawback of the cult of materialism is that it creates longings which can never be fully satisfied, for as soon as we buy a car we discover that to be socially accepted we must now become a member of a *two*-car family. In the same way the moment we finish making the repayments on a colour television set it becomes outmoded by the artificial process of planned obsolescence, which urges us to discard our functionally perfect piece of electronic equipment for a later model which offers an integral video recorder and the capacity to display four channels simultaneously on one split screen. This commercially manufactured discontent sells goods but creates tension.

When we arrive in this world we have very few inborn requirements, apart from the need to eat, drink, sleep, reproduce, play and satisfy our curiosity instinct. These are called *innate* needs. Primitive man was content providing these basic needs were satisfied. Not so Western man today, for we have developed other yearnings – for ocean-going yachts and gold-plated bathroom taps – which are culturally induced and so are termed *acquired* needs. As the industrial societies of the Western world have developed, these acquired yearnings have grown both in number and in strength. Our grandparents were content with a pony and trap for transport, a log fire for warmth and a pack of playing cards for evening entertainment. Our parents' needs were a little more sophisticated. They wanted to make their journeys by car, heat their homes by electricity and while away their winter hours playing Monopoly and backgammon. Our acquired needs have burgeoned. We feel cheated if we cannot circle the globe in supersonic aeroplanes, equip our homes with central heating and air conditioning and amuse ourselves with video games, satellite television and CD players with quadrophonic sound.

It is easy to argue that because of our material wealth we should be infinitely more contented than our forebears. And yet in practice, as a result of the explosion of our acquired needs, dissatisfaction is much more commonly experienced today than it was a century ago. If a water main burst outside my house and deprived me of my indoor water supply I would feel discomfited, and yet I have no doubt that my grandparents managed quite happily drawing their drinking water from an outside pump or well. So it is that today's luxuries become tomorrow's necessities.

Unfortunately material wealth, as well as being fragile and impermanent, is also subject to the economic law of diminishing marginal utility. If we are a hobo sleeping rough we are happy to be given a discarded pair of trousers, but if we already have a wardrobe full of clothes we gain little satisfaction from the gift of yet another pair of slacks. In the same way if we are a starving Biafran we are delighted to be given a handful of grain, but if we have just eaten a *cordon bleu* meal we find it difficult to wax enthusiastic about the offer of a box of hand-made chocolates. Children, in particular, quickly reach the point of satiation. This was proved more than fifty years ago when a psychologist took a group of over a thousand schoolchildren and tested their fondness for unadulterated cod liver oil. Some could not stand the taste of the fishy extract. Others found it a positive delicacy and when given the chance would cheerfully take 16 tablespoons a day to satisfy their craving. But if they kept to this level of consumption their desire soon dwindled and within a few days they chose to take less until they finally discovered that cod liver oil was no longer on their list of either wants or likes.

It is possible to have too much of a good thing, an observation which applies to most yearnings – except the insatiable yen for money. Even billionaires, who have enough money to satisfy every conceivable human requirement, still strive to increase the size of their fortunes. This is probably because in them the struggle to acquire money – which is a means to an end rather than an end in itself – has become a conditioned pattern of behaviour. Just as Pavlov's laboratory dogs were trained to salivate when a bell was rung, so the fortune hunters go on swelling the size of their bank accounts long after they have forgotten the initial stimulus which started them on their quest for financial security.

Psychologist J. B. Wolfe has shown how easy it is to develop the money-hoarding habit. He trained chimpanzees to work for poker chips, by teaching them initially that the tokens could be exchanged for a food reward. Quickly the chimps learned to acquire and hoard the valueless chips and would even resort to begging to augment their store. So it is with humans, who will work, beg, suffer, fight, cheat and steal to obtain money, which they are conditioned to seek for its own sake rather than for its exchange value. As the collection of wealth of itself brings no intrinsic physical satisfaction, this yearning is never satiated in the way that it is when youngsters over-indulge themselves in cod liver oil. As a result money is like sea water, the more you drink it the thirstier you become.

We cause ourselves considerable anxiety when we struggle to satisfy our ever-expanding range of acquired needs – money, luxury housing, fashionable clothing and expensive grown-up toys. In the process we make our lives unnecessarily complicated. We may run up a hefty debt to buy a suit at a time when our wardrobes are overflowing with perfectly wearable clothes. Most of us have enough shirts, blouses, skirts and trousers to last a lifetime, yet we continue to buy more. Henry David Thoreau, the nineteenth-century nature philosopher, urged his countrymen to cast off the burden of unnecessary wants. 'Simplicity, simplicity, simplicity' was his constant cry. He lived, ate and dressed simply. 'No man ever stood lower in my estimation for having a patch on his clothes; yet I am sure there is greater anxiety, commonly, to have fashionable clothes than to have a sound conscience. If my jacket and trousers are fit to worship God in, they will do, will they not? I say beware of any enterprise that requires new clothes, and not a new wearer of clothes.'

Others complicate their lives, not with the trappings of personal adornment, but with bricks and mortar. Their major concern is to buy a prestigious house stocked with luxury furnishings and fittings. Having done so they then embark on a never-ending round of home improvements which make heavier demands on their time and energy than ever before. We take an entire lifetime to repay a mortgage on a house. Neanderthal man could clear a temporary resting place in a cave within a few hours. A Red Indian could make a portable wigwam in two days and an industrious Eskimo could construct an igloo within a day, given favourable weather conditions.

During the latter part of his life Somerset Maugham owned the exquisitely appointed Villa Mauresque at Cap Ferrat. Here he dined off silver plate, served by a personal butler, footman and a staff of eleven servants. But the menage, for all its opulence, did not bring him any great satisfaction. When his nephew asked him what was the happiest memory of his life, Maugham stammered: 'I c-can't think of a single moment. I've been a f-failure the whole way through my life.' Even his wealth gave him little consolation.

'Though I'm a millionaire,' he admitted as he cast his eye around the villa, 'compared to some of my neighbours here on the Cap, I'm a *very poor* millionaire.' Like many owners of expensive real estate, Maugham gained less contentment from his luxurious life-style than Thoreau enjoyed in the primitive log hut he built beside the Walden Pond.

Contentment does not depend on what you have, but on what you can do without. Every now and again I like to rediscover the joys of the simple, unsophisticated life, stripped of aeroplanes, computers, telephones, cars and television sets. Putting a pack on my back I tramp through the countryside for several days on end, asking only for a place to quench my hunger and thirst by day, and a dry and cosy place to rest my head by night. During these few days as a 'vagabond' I restore my soul and reaffirm my priorities. Marlon Brando does much the same thing when he retreats to Tetiarao, the Pacific island he bought on the proceeds of his appearance in *Mutiny on the Bounty*. 'There,' he says, 'you have fish in the water, milk in the coconuts; the earth and the sky. Basics. It's important to realise how simple life can be – and still go on.'

We can be happy with little or miserable with much. A simple tub was enough for Diogenes; half the world insufficient for Alexander the Great. These days many people are so busy making a good living that they do not find time to make a good life. This can be a problem for dual-career families, if both husband and wife give so much to their work that they have nothing left to share with one another. Researchers at the University of North Carolina have found that men with high-achieving working wives have a three-times greater than average risk of suffering coronary disease. They attribute this to a decline in domestic peace and contentment, brought about when women return from a tiring day at the office and pass on some of the pressures of their work.

The true joys of life do not come from high salaries and material possessions but from an infinite variety of simple things – a child's smile, a glorious sunset, the good-humoured banter of a friend, a beautiful phrase of music or a moment of light-hearted play with a family pet. The more we complicate our lives, the less time we have for these simple, unsophisticated pleasures. The followers of Zen Buddhism find contentment by concentrating totally on the activities and tasks of the moment, however menial they may be. They do everything to the glory of God, whether it be cleaning their shoes, making a pot of tea or cooking a bowl of rice. Even Westerners can find nirvana in these prosaic activities, providing they are prepared to forget the troubles of yesterday, cease worrying constantly about the concerns of tomorrow, and immerse themselves completely and wholeheartedly in the simple joy of living in the 'here and now'. We cannot exist in the past or in the future, the only time we have to live is *now*. The teachings of preachers, politicians and economists have sometimes been misinterpreted in such a way that we have been prepared to sacrifice contemporary contentment for future gratification. Preachers have invited us to lead a life of self-denial with the promise of 'pie in the sky when we die'. Left-wing agitators have urged us to devote our lives to the building of a socialist utopia which they expect will emerge in the not-too-distant future. At the same time economists have sung the virtues of 'deferred gratification'. No doubt these philosophies have their merit, but while it is prudent to *work* for the future, it is vital to *live* in the present. If not, we suffer the fate which Ruskin described as 'bulb issuing in bulb but never in tulip'.

We travel through life like express trains, so anxious to get to our final destinations that we have no time for wayside halts. We are too busy to spend time with our friends. These are pleasures we will enjoy when our work slackens off, when we retire or when our ship comes home. But the tomorrow of deferred gratifications never comes.

When man invented the clock he created the weapon of his own destruction. The megalithic monuments of Stonehenge on Salisbury Plain represent one of man's earliest attempts to record the passage of time. Since that time our activities have become more and more closely geared to the relentless onward march of time. The Jews created one of the earliest working schedules, starting their day at 6 o'clock and setting aside three special periods for prayer, at 9 am, midday and 3 pm. By the fifth century BC, according to the Greek tragedies, man had begun to experience time urgency. This oppression grew greater still with the advent of the medieval monks, who divided the day into twelve hours, each named after the devotional work and prayers allotted to them, such as Matins, Lauds, Prime, Terce, Sext, Nones and Vespers. When accurate chronometers replaced sundials and hour glasses it became possible to work to still closer deadlines and to schedule appointments for 8.15 precisely instead of 'in the early forenoon'. In 1895, at the height of the Industrial Revolution, factory time clocks were created so that the comings and goings of workers could be timed to the second. A few years later Frank and Lillian Gilbreth subjected the daily labours of workers in various occupations to careful time-and-motion study, a scrutiny which gave greater prominence still to the inexorable march of time.

By now hassle and haste had become a major social affliction and recognised health hazard. In 1910 Sir William Osler gave a lecture in London to the Royal College of Physicians on the subject of *angina pectoris*. He reported that he had examined 269 patients with heart disease and found that they shared certain personality characteristics. They were highly ambitious, hard-working and driven by a chronic sense of time urgency. The same observations were made years later by Californian cardiologists Meyer Friedman and Ray Rosenman, who noted that patients suffering from heart disease were victims of a 'hurry sickness'. Their problem, according to Dr Friedman, 'arises from an insatiable desire to accomplish too much or to take part in too many events in the amount of time available'.

In their haste to move to pastures new, these jet-set nomads never find time to sample the here and now. Some while ago I was talking to an American tourist who had just returned from a whirlwind twenty-one day tour of Europe. 'Did you find time to visit Florence?' I asked. As the name evoked no immediate recollections he fumbled in his pocket for a notebook on which he had written his complete itinerary, together with a few brief notes of the places he had visited. Flicking through the pages he came to the section marked Italy. 'Yes,' he said, 'we visited Florence . . . and I liked it.' Apart from those few words in his travelogue no other memory remained of his visit to the birthplace of Renaissance culture.

I thought this was an extreme example of hurry sickness, until a friend told me of a remark he chanced to overhear in the National Gallery, London, when a testy Australian scolded her husband for delaying her whirlwind passage through London by stopping to look at the *Rokeby Venus*: 'Hurry up Arthur,' she said, 'we'll never get through this gallery if you keep stopping to look at the pictures.'

Many people today maintain this heedless pace through life, a hustle which is a characteristic of the industrial age, but totally unknown to the world of Nature. We live our lives by two entirely different chronological scales: 'natural' time and 'factitious' time. The first is the chronology of the seasons, the diurnal rhythms of night and day, the regular phases of the moon, the constant pattern of the tides, the eternal biological cycle of birth, life and death. The second is the man-made tempo of airline schedules, work deadlines, timetables, alarm clocks, three-day sales and sell-by dates. The one is permanent, unchanging and reassuring; the other chaotic and fleeting. Factitious time is often measured in seconds; natural time in aeons.

Excitement can be derived by chasing factitious time. Contentment comes from experiencing the serenity of natural time. We are harried when we rush to catch the 8.15 express, but we enjoy moments of contemplative peace whenever we stop to look around us and view the splendour of God's handiwork. The earth beneath us we often take for granted. When we bulldoze trees and hedges we may make dustbowls of our fields, forgetting that it takes practically a thousand years to make a single inch of soil. When we enter a cave, we wonder at the beauty of the stalagmites and stalactites, the petrified rock formations which grow at a rate of an inch every thousand years. When we toss a nugget of coal on the fire we recognise that we are burning the debris of forests which have been buried by time and crushed into stone by the sheer weight and heat of the earth's crust. Although this is one of the more rapid geological processes, it still took three million years to create the coalfield of South Wales.

People who remain close to Nature retain a precious sense of timelessness. I was reminded of this when I made a visit recently to the Republic of Ireland. Coming post-haste from the hurly-burly of London I was struck by the leisurely pace of the softly spoken Celtic folk. On my first night I watched incredulously as a barman took ten minutes to pull me a single pint of Guinness, stopping every few minutes to stand back to admire his work and let the creamy-white head settle. 'You've turned that into an art form,' I told him admiringly. 'And why not,' he replied. 'We don't hurry our pleasures here. When God made time he made plenty of it.' That simple philosophy is the perfect counter to 'hurry sickness'.

Our technological genius is alienating us from the world of Nature. We grew up in a garden of Eden where we were one with Nature; now we have severed our close connection with Mother Earth and have entered a concrete jungle bare of earth and fields and running water. Our contact with the natural kingdom is vicarious. It does not come from tilling the land or even rambling through the countryside, but from reading *The National Geographical Magazine* or watching wildlife documentaries on television. Whether we are driving a car, working in an office or relaxing in a home, there is always a pane of glass to separate us from the elements. We no longer feel the stimulus of rain and wind. With centrally heated offices and hermetically sealed, double-glazed, draught-excluded homes, we no longer have the chance to act and react with our environment.

This alienation is not experienced by primitive tribesmen, who still express a close communion with the natural world. Many continue to worship the sun and give thanks for the fertility of the soil. In their festivals they celebrate the regular alternation of the seasons. In rain storms the Indians of the North American plains will bare their bodies to the elements so they can 'be alone with the rain' and feel 'a unity with these tremendous forces'. In his autobiography Chief Standing Bear of the Sioux Indians tells of the empathy his people have for the world around them. 'We are of the soil and the soil is of us. We love the birds and beasts that grow with us on this soil. They drank the same water and breathed the same air. We are all one in nature.'

This feeling of oneness with Nature is the very essence of the transcendental experience which was aptly described by Freud as the 'oceanic feeling'. Town dwellers find it hard to develop this sense of mystic communion, although many endeavour to maintain a tenuous link with the natural world by filling their homes with symbols of their pastoral past – caged budgerigars, exotic house-plants and aquaria stocked with tropical fish.

The philosophies of the East bring contentment because they emphasise this fundamental human need for cosmic integration. The word 'yoga' means 'union', a fusion which is not brought about by *submerging* the identity of the individual, but by *merging* it with the world at large. A drop of dew shimmers briefly on a lotus leaf and then falls into the pool. From there it is carried by a stream until it eventually enters and merges with the mighty sea. So too we have our brief, individual existence, and also our permanent place as part of the oceanic whole. The same thought is a fundamental tenet of Buddhist doctrine. According to the *Dhammapada Buddha*: 'There is no difference between the sun and man. There is no such thing as my body, or your body, except in words. It is all one. Sun, mineral, man.'

We find it more difficult to experience this 'oceanic feeling', for the cultures of the West place their emphasis on individual identity and development, rather than on cosmic unity. As a result of this fragmentation we suffer what William James referred to as *Zerrissenheit*, meaning 'torn-to-pieces-hood'. Martin Buber, the Israeli theologian, attempted to overcome this alienation. Our relationships with the outside world can be expressed in one of two basic ways, he explained. Either we observe an I-it relationship, or an I-Thou relationship. In the first case we divorce ourselves from the rest of creation, in the second we make ourselves an integral part of the cosmic whole. This concept arose in Buber's mind when he was still a boy and passionately fond of riding. One day he was grooming his favourite horse when he experienced a sudden feeling of overwhelming joy. In a moment of instant empathy he knew not only what it felt like to be an eleven-year-old lad stroking the neck of a horse, but also what it felt like to be a horse fondled by a boy. This ecstatic feeling transcended the boundaries of time and space and formed the basis of his later philosophical teaching.

Perhaps our growing interest in ecology will make it easier for us to adopt an I-Thou relationship with the world around us. If so it will enable us to assume a more genuinely holistic approach to life. At present we tend to think of holism as the harmonious integration of an individual's body, mind and spirit. This outlook is not truly holistic, even though it is certainly an improvement on the Cartesian dichotomy of body and mind. The Chinese and Red Indians have a much wider concept of holism. For them the vital integration consists of a synthesis of mind, body, spirit – and universe.

The adoption of this world-embracing outlook breeds contentment, and as a result, fosters health. It is no coincidence that the words 'hale, whole and holy' all stem from the same etymological root. So far there is no concrete *proof* that a holistic philosophy predisposes to health, but there is considerable evidence that people are healthier when they follow a recognised spiritual faith. One survey showed that regular church-goers, irrespective of whether they smoked or drank, had lower-than-average rates of high blood pressure, heart disease, cervical cancer, tuberculosis, emphysema and cancer of the rectum. The death rate from coronary disease, for instance, was 60 per cent lower in men who were frequent attenders at religious services than in those who never or rarely attended church. Another study of nearly 14,000 Protestant clergymen, carried out by a University of Washington research team, revealed that non-conformist ministers in America have death rates 30 per cent lower than the national average. Even though some smoked, and many lived in highly industrialised areas, it was found that the men of God were five times less likely to die from lung cancer than the average white American. Their risk of suffering fatal cancers of the stomach and intestines was also much below the national average.

Dr Meyer Friedman made a similar observation when he examined the life-styles of a small group of middle-aged women with heart disease. With the exception of one of the women who was a nun, he noted, 'None of them expresses true confidence that there is any Supreme Being who is watching over them *as a loving, totally forgiving, and accepting Father*, even though several of them had actively tried to believe.'

Contentment is an antidote for anxiety and stress, which some find by following a religious faith, others by adopting Albert

Schweitzer's simple philosophy of showing 'reverence for life'. For some contentment comes from relinquishing their dependence on material possessions, for others from leading a simple life or escaping the clutches of 'hurry sickness'. Some acquire their peace of mind in childhood, others attain it later in life by patient self-training. This can be done by taking certain practical steps:

- **Learn To Be Patient**
  *Impatience is one of the major enemies of contentment. There is so much we want to do – so many goals to attain, skills to learn, heights to scale and places to visit – that we become frustrated if we are held up for even a single minute in our endless quest for instant satisfaction. Yet we cannot have everything at the imperious wave of a magic wand. Many things cannot be hurried. Some take time, or the co-operation of other people. Others can only occur when conditions are ripe. Car drivers become agitated when they are held up in a traffic jam, but their frustration does nothing to speed the rate of traffic flow. Punctuality has been called the politeness of kings, but if your train is late, or your car breaks down, it may be impossible to keep an appointment on time. Such misfortunes cannot be improved by fretting and fuming. When Mayor Jimmy Walker of New York was unavoidably detained on his way to a public meeting he kept cool by saying: 'If you're there before it's over, you're there on time.'*

  *If we are not prepared to do this occasionally we are doomed to waste our time in futile endeavour. Some years ago I watched two fishermen wade towards their boats which were stranded on the mud flats of a coastal estuary. One was so impatient to get to sea that he hauled his boat over fifty yards of oozing mud to get it launched. The other was more sanguine. He occupied himself for a few minutes preparing his lines by which time the tide had come in and automatically floated his boat, a splendid illustration of the maxim: 'Everything comes to he who waits'.*

  *The world today is filled with activists, anguishing over their desire to bring an instant end to social injustices. They want to stop animal cruelty today. Banish atmospheric pollution now. Bring an immediate halt to poverty, war, malnutrition, racial* discrimination, illiteracy, child prostitution and drug abuse. These are laudable goals, but impossible time scales. Providing we work and wait these social improvements will be made – if not in our lifetime then in that of our offspring. The wealth of the Roman Empire depended on the daily work of 60 million slaves, a practice which must have been abhorrent to Christ and his disciples. Yet they did not speak out against the vile practice, because they recognised that the principle of slave labour had the support of the vast majority of the Roman population. The abolition of slavery from the civilised world came centuries later – when the time was ripe.

If we do not show patience, we will inevitably suffer disappointment and frustration. On some occasions we must learn to practise the oriental art of non-striving, for sometimes our goals will most easily be attained by adopting the 'slowly, slowly, catchee monkey' approach. At other times we will be more likely to succeed if we stop meddling altogether and follow a policy of total non-involvement. This strategy was frequently recommended by Lao Tze. 'Who is there who can make muddy water clear?' he asked his followers. 'If you leave it alone it will come clear of itself.' Patience like this is undoubtedly a virtue, cultivated in the East but sadly undervalued in the Western world today.

- ## Take Your Time
  'Hurry sickness' is the root cause of much unhappiness and stress-related illness. It can be eradicated by making a conscious effort to slow down. God made time, but man made haste. When we programme our day's activities we should always leave generous space for reflection. Why should we crowd our day with work so that we have no time to think, no chance to play and no opportunity to stop and smell the roses? Why should we allow ourselves to be caught up in the crazy pace of contemporary life? No two people have the same rhythm of work. Some are happier when they are running, others when they are ambling. The wise individual sets his own pace and refuses to be hustled by outside interference.

*Often we act in haste and repent in leisure. Most radio stations allow a few seconds delay in the transmission of live, phone-in conversations so that the producer can censor obscene or libellous comments. We should introduce a similar pause between stimulus and response, counting up to ten rather than rushing to say, do, or decide anything which might be the cause for later regret. Whenever I am roused to write an angry letter I follow a strict rule of never posting it immediately, but leaving it unopened overnight. In the morning, when my temper has cooled and I have had a chance to sleep on the matter, I read the letter again. Quite often I find that the mere fact of composing the diatribe is enough to get the matter off my chest. In this case I tear the letter up and toss it into the waste-basket where it can do no harm. If not, and I still feel as strongly about the issue, the letter gets signed, sealed and posted.*

*The Sanhedrin, the supreme court of justice in ancient Jerusalem, observed a similar precaution against precipitate action. Criminal cases were tried during the day and could be completed before nightfall providing the victim was found to be innocent. But where guilt was proved a night had to pass before sentence was given. This allowed time for reflection and ensured that dispassionate judgements were given.*

*We need time to act wisely and we also need time to behave compassionately. This was proved at Princeton University, when a group of theological students was unwittingly cajoled into re-enacting the story of the Good Samaritan. Each of the students was asked to prepare a short talk about the Good Samaritan, which had to be recorded in a room at the opposite end of the campus. Some were told that they were late for their recording appointment, others that they were expected shortly, and a third group that they could wander over whenever they were ready. As they crossed the campus they met an accomplice of the researchers, who was slumped in a doorway coughing and groaning. Fewer than half the group stopped to give the man aid, and these modern Good Samaritans were nearly all drawn from the unhurried group, showing that we need time not only to think but also to act as decent caring human beings.*

*If we devote ourselves solely to work, we deny ourselves the* finer things of life. This is beautifully expressed in an Old English prayer:

Take time to be friendly – it is the road to happiness.
Take time to dream – it is hitching your waggon to a star.
Take time to love and be loved – it is the privilege of the gods.
Take time to look around – it is too short a day to be selfish.
Take time to laugh – it is the music of the soul.

People who find space for these simple activities are likely to be most truly human and most surely healthy. Hence the importance of avoiding 'hurry sickness' and the wisdom of Thoreau's advice: 'Nothing can be more useful to a man than a determination not to be hurried.'

- **Live In the Present**

Contentment can never be found by bemoaning the past or fretting about the future. Contentment comes from total commitment to the 'here and now'. For centuries religious mystics have recognised that this is the pathway to transcendental bliss. Thomas Merton, the Catholic theologian, emphasised that by living in the present – a practice he called 'nowness' – we can both find ourselves and lose ourselves in the cosmic whole. A human being asserts its individuality, and serves its divine purpose, said Merton, when it 'gives glory to God by being what He wants it to be here and now'. In the process we achieve a oneness with Nature, for the present moment, whether we are in a Trappist cell or a crowded supermarket, contains all that is necessary to achieve a union between the 'I' and the transcendental whole.

But the principle of 'nowness' has a practical, secular value as well as a purely mystical significance. Psychologist Abraham Maslow stressed that individuals must be totally absorbed in what they are doing if they are to achieve their full potential. He quoted a schoolmistress who confessed to being 'utterly lost in the present' while she was teaching her class a new method of reading. 'This ability to become "lost in the present" ,' Maslow wrote, 'seems to be a sine qua non for creativeness of any kind.'

Being utterly absorbed in the present is also a valuable

*technique for coping with stress. While we are focusing our minds on a game of bridge, or savouring the taste of a mouthful of Earl Grey tea, we cannot at the same time be worrying about bank overdrafts, business crises or family concerns. Napoleon learnt this technique at an early stage in his career. 'When I have done with one subject,' he wrote, 'I close the compartment drawer, and open another, so that my various jobs never overlap one another, and there is neither confusion nor fatigue.' Others find it helpful to commit their worries to paper, and to prepare a comprehensive list of each day's chores, so they can tackle them one at a time. This method is favoured by entrepreneur Mark McCormack, who wrote the best-selling book* What They Don't Teach You at Harvard Business School. *'I have learnt to compartment-alise my business emotions as well as my business day,' he reports. 'I write everything down, and since I put my notes where I know they will pop up again in the right place and at the right time, once I have written something down I forget about it. The end result is that when I break from work, I break from work-related stress as well.'*

*Ace athletes know that they must follow a similar mental drill if they are to function at their best. A golfer must treat each stroke in isolation and not allow himself to be unsettled by his appalling mistake at the previous hole, when he missed a simple, nine-inch putt. The same applies to tennis players who must regard each shot as an entirely separate entity, regardless of whether they are beginning to feel complacent with a five-nil lead, or starting to seize up with nerves as they shape up to serve to save a match point. If we live each day as a separate entity we escape the disappointments of the past and avoid the dreadful expectations of the future. This was the policy explorer Robert Swann adopted when he led his team on their successful trek to the South Pole. 'To guard against discouragement,' he recorded, 'we followed a cardinal rule: Every day was treated entirely separately and on its own.'*

*Paradoxically, if we learn to live in the 'here and now', we experience a feeling of timelessness, because forever is merely a never-ending succession of timeless present moments. We get our sense of hurry only when we view 'now' in juxtaposition with* the rapidly passing moments of yesterday and the fast approaching moments of tomorrow. My favourite definition of eternity was given by Boethius, a Roman writer who had great influence in the Middle Ages but is very seldom mentioned today. 'Eternity,' he wrote in a text first translated into English by King Alfred, 'is the possession of all time, past, present and to come, in full plenitude, in a single moment here and now.' Those who can achieve that feeling of 'nowness' will find an escape from 'hurry sickness' and a gateway to peace of mind. I have a Latin motto pinned above my desk to provide a constant reminder of the need to live each day to the full: *Carpe diam* (Reap the day).

- ## See Life In Its Historical Perspective
It is easy to regard our daily problems as unique and overwhelming. Yet there are few catastrophes which have not been experienced before and none which have not been previously surmounted. 'There is no new thing under the sun', was the way Ecclesiastes the Preacher expressed this fundamental truth. The knowledge that thousands before us have shared our trials and tribulations and coped successfully with them, should give us hope and reassurance.

The present may be different from the past, but in essence it is neither better nor worse. It has its heroes and its rogues; its sinners and its saints; its times of triumph and its moments of disaster. If we take an irrationally pessimistic view of the contemporary scene, we become unnecessarily despondent. Some people do this habitually, like the man Oscar Wilde encountered on one of his American lecture tours. 'How lovely the moon is,' Wilde eulogised as he gazed up at the cloudless night sky. 'You should have seen it before the war,' was the American's laconic reply.

The person who sees things in historical perspective realises that nothing is new and nothing of overwhelming importance or lasting significance. Dr Johnson gave his friend Boswell sound advice when he told him how to put his petty, day-to-day worries into proper perspective. 'Sir,' he said, 'consider how insignificant this will appear a twelve-month hence.'

## • Forget the Errors Of the Past

*Chronic remorse is one of the most tiring activities known to man, and one of the least productive. Many of my patients carry with them an enormous burden of guilt. Some blame themselves because they should have been kinder to their parents before they died. Others never cease to regret the way they educated their children. A number feel guilty because of past misdemeanours; perhaps they jilted an old lover, were unfaithful to their husband, stole from an employer, had an abortion, tried to commit suicide or contracted venereal disease when they were young adults. These past indiscretions play on their mind and warp their self-esteem. But no human being is perfect. We all err. In fact our passage through life is rather like the progress of a drunk staggering down a narrow alleyway. We try desperately to follow a straight-and-narrow path, but as we advance we inevitably stumble from time to time and regularly veer from side to side. Like the inebriate, we advance by making a series of repeated course corrections. This does not matter providing we eventually arrive at our chosen goal. But some people are more conscious of their temporary lapses than of their overall achievements. They judge themselves to be failures because they have failed over one particular issue. They consider themselves unlovable because they have been unable to win the love of one or two key people in their lives. By focusing their attention on their past mistakes, failings and humiliations they make themselves perennially discontented. Far kinder to let each fresh day wash out the discouragements of the past, just as the tide washes out footprints on the sand and leaves its surface pristine, fresh and clear.*

*When we make mistakes we should admit our errors, make amends for any damage we have done and do our best to learn from the experience so that we do not commit the same mistakes again. Then we need to forgive and forget. This is where many people fail, for they do not realise that the process of forgetting is every bit as therapeutic as the rites of confession and absolution. Equally importantly, it must be remembered that the act of forgiving ourselves is as vital for our long-term mental health as the* more widely recognised virtue of finding forgiveness for others. Rolling in the mud is never the best way of getting clean.

One New York psychiatrist considered that his major contribution lay in helping his patients to free themselves from the recriminations of the past. Toward the end of his long and distinguished career he claimed that two simple words formed the foundation of many people's psychic troubles; and two equally simple words offered them a practical escape from their distress. Throughout his years in practice he found that many people exhaust themselves by wallowing in self-pity and personal regrets. Their favourite two words were 'If only . . .': 'If only I'd taken the university place that was offered me', 'If only I hadn't devoted so much time to my work', 'If only I'd travelled a little more'. By dwelling on these past mistakes they marred their present and jeopardised their future. To overcome this constant emotional drain he suggests that we should bar the words 'if only' from our vocabularies. Instead we should substitute the words 'next time'. This gives us a far more positive outlook on life and offers us a practical way of overcoming our frustrations and failings. 'Next time' we will take the educational opportunities that are available to us. 'Next time' we will be less obsessed with our work and find more time for leisure-time pursuits.

By adopting this technique we close the door on mistakes of the past, and make it possible to focus our time, thoughts and energy on the present and future.

- ## Strive To Be Humble
Disappointment is lessened if we view the cosmos as a whole and recognise our utter insignificance in the vast eternity of time and space. We suffer when we get puffed up with our own importance and languish when we grotesquely enlarge the significance of our personal cares and woes. Scientists have calculated that even if every human being on earth were six feet tall and a foot and a half wide they could still be packed in a box no bigger than a half mile square. In that neat package the entire population of the globe could be pushed off the top of the Grand Canyon and lost from view for ever. This puts mankind – generals, kings, queens and

*emperors – into its proper perspective. Atomic physicists regard us as even more ethereal. They see the human body as a largely empty space, set in a vast universal space which is even emptier of solid substance. According to their calculations, if it were possible to eliminate the voids between the electrons and nuclei which make up each atom of our bodies, it would be possible to condense every human being into a particle of solid matter no bigger than a grain of sand. So much for our dreams of omnipotence and our delusions of grandeur. In fact, say the physicists, these seemingly solid bodies of ours are merely empty shells filled with tiny particles which throb with energy in rhythm with the myriad pulsating movements of every other structure on earth, combining as they do so in what is poetically described as the 'bio-dance of the universe'.*

*Sometimes we allow ourselves to be bedazzled by our technical genius, but even here we have no cause for pride. We may have learnt to harness nuclear energy, which is a creditable achievement, but we still have not discovered a source of power which begins to compare with the enormous forces liberated by earthquakes, tempests and tidal waves. In a single minute a hurricane expends more energy than the American people consume in electricity in fifty years.*

*If we pursue self-aggrandisement we will reap disappointment and despair; if we seek humility we will find contentment.*

- **Learn To Live Simply**
*Much of the discontent we experience today comes from our unfulfilled desires. The entire might of the advertising industry is combined to make us dissatisfied with what we have. A schoolboy wants a larger bike, his mother longs for a cashmere coat, his sister craves a TV set for her bedroom, his father envies his neighbour's Jaguar car. The more numerous our unfulfilled wants the greater our dissatisfaction. This is recognised in the Hindu teaching: 'When you learn not to desire, you will rise above suffering.' St Thomas à Kempis reached a similar conclusion when he observed: 'Forego desire and you shall find peace.'*

*Socrates recognised this truth and made a practice of living* frugally, even to the point of travelling barefoot. But even he could not resist the lure of the market-place. One of his friends could not understand why he spent time viewing the tempting goods which he resolutely refused to buy. Socrates' reply was simple: 'I am always amazed to see how many things I can do without.' The less we laden ourselves with physical possessions and material needs the faster we travel and the less we have to worry about.

For centuries it has been customary in the West to look outside for satisfaction. Sailors circumnavigated the globe to find the wealth of the Indies; migrants joined the gold rush to the Yukon; disillusioned Londoners emigrated to Australia to seek their fortune; impoverished Scots trekked to London where they believed the streets were paved with gold. All expected to find happiness in a crock of gold buried at the end of their particular rainbows. The traditional Oriental knows better. Their philosophies lead them to believe that nirvana does not lie in some far-off utopia, but will be found within themselves. The good life we all crave, of peace and contentment, exists the moment we stop wanting something better.

Artur Rubinstein, the eminent pianist, was desperately unhappy as a teenage virtuoso. He wanted so much and felt he had secured so little that he eventually made an unsuccessful suicide attempt. He took a belt from an old dressing-gown, secured one end to a hook on the wall and tied the other securely round his neck. But the belt snapped and he tumbled to the ground unhurt. Soon after this merciful escape Rubinstein discovered the secret of contentment. 'One fine morning, there I was – come to life again,' he recalled. 'I opened my eyes on a brand new world for, after all, to escape death is to be re-born in a way. The sight of a flower moved me, seeing a dog chasing its shadow down the street brought tears to my eyes . . . What was I waiting for to be happy? That was happiness, the humble daily provender: I had held it in my hand and had never been aware of it.'

Like Rubinstein we find contentment if we limit our desires and find our satisfaction in the simple things of life.

- **Enjoy the Beauties of Nature**

*One simple way of overcoming tension is to withdraw from time to time from the ephemeral, concrete world of noise and hassle and take refuge in the tranquillity and permanence of Nature. Whenever he has a break from his royal duties Prince Charles slips away to Highgrove, his farm in Gloucestershire, where he finds the farmwork 'therapeutic'. As he told a television interviewer: 'I find it marvellous actually to get down to mucking out, milking cows, delivering calves and mending stone walls. It's certainly a complete change from the kind of existence I lead. Somehow it straightens out your whole attitude to life.' Others find a similar peace from gardening, fishing or country walking.*

*Goethe spent his entire lifetime writing the classic story of Faust, the scholar who was so desperate to find contentment that he made a pact with the Devil to sell his soul in return for one moment of bliss on earth when he could genuinely say: 'Let this moment linger, it is so good.' So Faust began his endless search for pleasure which he expected to find from sexual conquests, travel, political power and the accumulation of material wealth. To his dismay, after exercising his superhuman power and amassing riches and an endless tally of sexual seductions, he found that genuine contentment still eluded him. Finally, as an elderly man he discovered the joys of Nature. Goethe started writing his masterpiece at the age of twenty. He finished it just before he died at the age of eighty-three. Now, with a lifetime's experience behind him, he knew without doubt where his character must turn to find peace of mind. So, in the final pages of his epic tale, he depicts Faust draining a patch of land and creating a garden. Here he finds contentment. Now for the first time he achieves his life-long goal and can truly say: 'Let this moment linger, it is so good.'*

*We need to look at the world around us with the wonderment of a child. Think how marvellous the stars would appear if we were seeing them for the first time. Imagine how glorious a rose would seem if we had been blind from birth and had just regained our sight. Think how precious an evening sunset would appear if we knew it was the last one we would see. Helen Keller, the blind American author, gave this invaluable advice to everyone engaged in the Faustian quest for true contentment: 'Use your eyes as if tomorrow you would be stricken blind, hear the music of voices, the song of a bird, as if you would be stricken deaf tomorrow. Touch each object as if tomorrow your tactile sense would fail. Smell the perfume of flowers, taste with relish each morsel, as if tomorrow you could never smell and taste again.'*

- ## Learn to Accept the Inevitable

*Every moment of our lives we have a choice: either we accept our current circumstances or we struggle to change them. Supposing I lost an eye in a car accident, either I could be angry and resentful at my misfortune, or I could accept the disability knowing that it could not be altered by medical treatment. The first reaction would be self-destructive since it would generate non-productive frustration and stress. The second response would minimise the effect of the emotional trauma and enable me to make the quickest possible adaptation to the unfortunate accident. Many people are discontented because they cannot make this second choice. They are incapable of coming to terms with the inevitable. Instead of making a bouquet with the flowers within their grasp, they are constantly looking for bigger and better blooms in someone else's garden.*

*Some races are schooled to accept their lot. When Lady Luck deals a Spaniard a poor hand of cards he accepts his fate with a shrug of the shoulders. 'Que sera, sera,' he says resignedly, 'what will be, will be.' Likewise the Thais. Their favourite phrase when they meet with misfortune is mai pen rai, meaning 'never mind it does not matter'. Psychiatrist Karl Menninger regarded this resignation as an 'inner strength'. So too did William James who referred to it as the 'religion of healthy-mindedness'. We can spend a lifetime harbouring resentments over misfortunes we can never amend: we were born with a cleft palate, our parents died when we were small, our education was interrupted by the war, poverty prevented us from going to university, a childhood illness stopped us becoming successful athletes. Mishaps like these must be willingly accepted, since they cannot be wilfully overcome.*

Professor Hans Selye, in the course of his work on stress research, demonstrated that there were two basic responses to stressful situations, the syntoxic and the catatoxic. When we show a syntoxic reaction we activate the tranquillising power of our neurohormonal system. This creates, in Selye's words, 'a state of passive tolerance which permits a kind of symbiosis, or peaceful co-existence with aggressors'. When we employ the catatoxic reaction we utilise the body's reserves to fight the aggressor or pathogen. Obviously there are times when one of these reactions is more appropriate than the other. Suppose we are attacked by unfair criticism. Our immediate gut response may be to fight back catatoxically. We want to punish the person who has subjected us to all this unjust contumely. But a moment's reflection may reveal that this is not the wisest course of action. If we counter-attack, we will give our critic the satisfaction of knowing that we have been wounded by his verbal vendetta, which may encourage him to continue or even intensify his assault. In addition, by prolonging the argument, we give his comments wider circulation. Far better, generally, to treat such criticism with dignified disdain.

Abraham Lincoln was subjected at times to bitter condemnation for his conduct during the American Civil War. This he bore with great fortitude. 'If the end brings me out all right,' he explained to a friend, 'what is said against me won't amount to anything. If the end brings me out wrong, ten angels swearing I was right would make no difference.'

At other times injustices should be fought rather than accepted with meek resignation. Whatever the situation we face, our bodies offer us the option of making either a syntoxic or a catatoxic response. Our health and happiness depends on the wisdom of that choice. In our search for contentment we should bear in mind the ancient prayer: 'God grant me the strength to change the things that need changing; the courage to accept the things that cannot be changed, and the wisdom to know the difference.'

Chapter Fifteen:

# THE INTEGRATED PERSONALITY

In the first seven chapters of this book I provided evidence to prove that a healthy mental attitude is the single most important factor in the promotion of health and the prevention of disease. This is not to say that we can now throw caution to the wind and forget about dieting, keeping slim and taking plenty of regular exercise. These precautions are still relevant, but the fundamental message of recent medical research is that the pursuit of physical fitness is far less important than the cultivation of a healthy attitude of mind. It is preferable to be a contented lounge lizard than an angry jogger; better to be chubby and cheerful than slim and sour.

Most people today have a very clear idea of the things they must do to keep in good *physical* condition. They know in intimate detail the foods they should eat and the foods they should avoid. They are well aware of the dangers of smoking and excessive drinking. Their urgent need now is for guidance on how to keep *mentally* fit.

Our underlying attitudes of mind have a profound effect on our health, our personal relationships, our success at work and even on our expectation of life. To achieve our full potential as individuals we must establish healthy habits of thought. As further research is carried out on this vital subject we will undoubtedly learn more about the effect of mental attitudes on human health, happiness, physical function and social well-being. These new discoveries will amplify and expand the principles enumerated in this book, which is merely a preliminary exploration of an exciting new approach to health and healing, which might well be described as Attitude Therapy. Although these concepts are still in a formative stage, there is nothing temporary or tentative about the Seven b-Attitudes of Health. These are the unchanging, central core of life-enhancing mental attitudes which have been extolled by generations of sages, philosophers and religious teachers. As such they are unlikely to undergo fundamental change in the future. Whatever modifications may be made in our understanding of Attitude Therapy, it is safe to assume that successful human beings will always be recognised by their possession of these seven basic qualities – they are committed, calm, confident, companionable, optimistic, cheerful and contented.

The widespread promotion of these seven qualities will improve the health and well-being of individuals. It will also be of vast benefit to society itself, because any group of people – family, business, club, neighbourhood, professional organisation, military unit, church fellowship or nation – which practises the Seven b-Attitudes will automatically create a happier and more united community, which both loves more and cares more.

Some people may feel that the practice of Attitude Therapy demands the piety of a saint, the self-discipline of an ascetic and the fortitude of a polar explorer. But in fact it requires no more than simple habit training. Since we have to take occasional thought for the future we can as easily train ourselves to look ahead with optimism as to view the future with despair. Since most of us identify definite goals and aspirations, it is as easy to select targets which are likely to bring us contentment as to choose those which are likely to bring us disappointment. First we shape the mental attitudes of our choosing, then forever afterwards the attitudes shape us.

Within every one of us there are the psychological resources we require to enrich our lives. All we need to do is foster them and bring them to the fore. A delightful story is told of a visit Michelangelo made to a builder's yard where he spotted a slab of misshapen marble. 'What are you planning to do with this?' he asked the builder. When he was told that the block had been discarded because it was too flawed to be of practical use he asked to have it delivered to his studio. 'It certainly is not useless,' the master replied. 'There is an angel imprisoned within it and I must set it free.' That is true of all of us. Inside us there are powerful, therapeutic emotions which are merely waiting to be activated and released. We do not need to take psychotropic drugs or undergo prolonged courses of psychotherapy, we merely need to release the mental component of the *medicatrix naturae.*

If we care about our health and happiness we must take steps to bring these therapeutic psychic forces into play. This is a responsibility which we cannot shelve or delegate. We cannot pass the responsibility for our well-being to the state or to doctors and psychiatrists. People are often tempted to play the role of helpless patient, but when they do so they relinquish the control of their destiny without freeing themselves of the onus of self-determination. By becoming dependent on therapies and therapists they do not shed the ultimate burden of responsibility; they merely sacrifice some of their personal autonomy. We are what we think. This is the vital determinant which shapes our health and moulds our destiny, which we alone can control.

We are currently witnessing a welcome return to the Greek concept of holistic medicine, a therapeutic outlook which embraces a harmonious conjunction of body, mind and spirit. Our next advance will be made when we adopt the principles outlined in this book, which recognise that well-being depends not only on the harmonious union of soma, psyche and spirit but also on the harmony established between individuals and their social and cosmic environments. To achieve our full potential for health and happiness we need to be at peace not only with ourselves but also with the world around us. Only then can we consider ourselves well-integrated individuals, a word derived from the Latin *integralis*, meaning 'whole'. This should be our aim, for therein lies our destiny.

# INDEX